ONE NURSE AT A TIME:

On A Mission

A Personal Journey into the Heart of Humanitarian Nursing

By Sue Averill and Elizabeth Coulter

One Nurse At A Time is a non-profit organization that helps nurses become involved in volunteer work. We believe that nurses are pebbles, which, when dropped into the pond, make far-reaching ripples. If we can put more nurses into the world, we will exponentially impact healthcare for those most in need.

For more information, please go to www.OneNurseAtATime.org

To contact us for speaking events, book clubs or questions about volunteering:
OneNurseAtATime@gmail.com

These stories are based on real events; however, names, places and other details have been changed for the sake of privacy. The views and opinions expressed by the authors of this book do not necessarily reflect the views of One Nurse At A Time.

ISBN: 978-0-9977325-1-1

Dedicated to nurses everywhere who never lose heart.

Contents

Introduction

I met Sue Averill while working in a Seattle Emergency Room in 2003. She had the reputation of being a nurse with strong clinical skills and a fierce patient advocate. I'd heard of her travels to Africa, Asia and other less travelled parts of the world, but hadn't really had a chance to speak to her about them until 2004. She was on her way to Liberia, where civil war had pushed over a million people into barren displacement camps.

"What's your motivation for going on these trips?" I asked before she left. She let out a laugh as if I'd asked a most ridiculous question.

It would take years for me to fully understand the answer to that question. Sue would travel, usually for months at a time, to places few of us will ever see. Each time she came back a calmer, more centered person.

How could this be when she'd seen, first hand, the cruelty powerful people can impose on weaker people within their own countries? She'd taken care of people in despicable conditions: refugees held in without hope in camps of fifty thousand and more; people who were guilty of the crime of being in the wrong place at the wrong time; people tortured and disfigured by child soldiers; the child soldiers who themselves were victims, having been kidnapped from their villages; women victims of violent crimes who had been beaten and raped. Yet when Sue returned from her missions, she did so with renewed energy and commitment to nursing.

These stories are not a Pollyanna version of mission life. They are strong and gritty, but sprinkled with compassion and humor, weapons of survival for an Emergency Room Nurse. In "They Are There" you will hear victims' accounts of the Lord's Resistance Army in Northern Uganda. In "Snap Judgment" you will find yourself in the aftermath of a battle of the civil war in Sudan. Another story will have you donning your protective suit before entering an Ebola treatment center in Sierra Leone, where one misstep could result in critical illness. You'll see lives transformed by simple plastic surgeries in Lahore, Pakistan. Finally, "Of Mugs and Men" tells the story of unexpected consequences when a pink kitty mug goes missing.

Yet these stories merely scratch the surface of the work done by humanitarian men and women around the world. People who, at great personal risk, stand against oppressive forces to help the most vulnerable and victimized. The recent bombings of hospitals in Afghanistan, Syria and Yemen reveal the risks these selfless people take so that medical care can be delivered to those suffering amidst war and famine.

Read these stories and you will find the answer to the question I asked so many years ago: *What's your motivation?*

Perhaps you will find a way to forge your own road to help others, even as we live in uncertain times in our country. Simple acts of kindness can go a long way in changing the world around us.

The proceeds of this book will be donated to One Nurse At A Time, an organization formed to help nurses discover their own path in volunteering. The time is ripe to rise up and take a step of empowerment to change the world.

If not now....when?

Elizabeth Coulter
Seattle, 2017

On that life changing mission to Lahore, I briefly put my finger on the pulse of humanity. I marveled that the spark that became "me" landed not in Pakistan, but in America, to parents who believed a girl can be anything she wants; to parents who encouraged and supported my independence and individuality.

When given so much through no merit of our own, is it not incumbent on each of us to account for our lives? To ask: What have I done for others?

— Sue Averill

Snippets from a First Mission:
Habila Town, Darfur, Sudan 2004

Earliest Days

The air is dry as Melba toast. I drink water constantly but rarely pee – a mixed blessing since there are only squat latrines and no toilets. My skin is scaly and cracked. My contact lenses feel like they're melting into my dry eyeballs. The toxic smoke from the evening cooking fires and burning garbage sends us into fits of hacking. My nose bleeds constantly, and everything snaps with static electricity. My hair stands on end like a science experiment. The DVD drives in the laptops die in the heat unless we cool them with ice packs.

There is no running water in our village. A teenage boy pumps water from one of the deep wells, repeatedly fills a twenty liter plastic jerry can and pours it into two black rubber sacks hanging down each side of a scruffy, sad-faced little donkey. He walks the donkey to our compound and reverses the process to empty the sacks into our side-lying-ex-oil-drums-turned-water-storage tanks. We have two hand wash stations and another for dishes and laundry. The boy lugs water up ten steps to a platform where the sun warms a water drum, providing us the luxury of warm, gravity-fed showers in the evening.

Our cook Nazra boils water for 30 minutes in a huge aluminum pot on a charcoal fire. She sets it aside until morning and then pours it through filters into storage containers for drinking. We have two "Sudanese refrigerators" – clay pots of water, cooling bottles of soda or water by evaporation.

I hate being new and unsure.

Just because the malaria mosquito is resistant to Chloroquine in Darfur doesn't prevent the drug from being sold in the markets. An emaciated old man limped to our health center with a hip abscess from injecting the thick oral syrup as a cure. After giving an IV sedative but paying little attention to basic cleanliness or sterility, the Sudanese doctor sliced into the puckered skin. Pus splattered the wall across the room. He dug inside the wound with a bare finger and grabbed instruments, packages of gauze and irrigating fluids with blood-covered hands. This man is a "trained medical professional." I have a lot of teaching to do.

I feel like the Pied Piper. The doc and I try to walk the village, but within five minutes we're impeded front, back and sides by dozens of children, darting and chirping like birds. "Sue Sue

How are you? Sue Sue What is your name? Sue Sue Good morning teacher! Sue Sue I am fine." They stare open mouthed at my white skin, but are terrified when I extend my hand for a touch. We climb the slight rise at the entrance to Habila, but kids dance up the rocks before we can reach the top.

There is no peace, much less quiet.

The animals of Darfur can be categorized in terms of value:

Horses are gold bullion. Prized above all else.

Camels are stocks and bonds. Highly valued and may be traded if necessary.

Cows are Certificates of Deposit. Mid-range holdings that hedge inflation.

Donkeys are hundred dollar bills. Worth keeping but can be spent or exchanged if necessary.

Goats and sheep are twenties. Plentiful.

Chickens are petty cash. Easy.

A village's wellbeing can be estimated by looking at the numbers and types of animals. Nomads owned horses and camels, and rode them proudly through the village. Wealthy men owned small herds of cattle, and laborers plied their trades on donkey-back. Goats and sheep were everywhere, but chickens were hard to find. Habila was inhabited by mostly displaced persons and was poor by animal banking standards.

There are no paved roads, only sand. The "vehicles" in town (besides a few for the military, UN, NGOs and one private motorcycle) are horses, camels, donkeys and bicycles. A woman rides a donkey with wood baskets holding precious cargo. A man leads a donkey with a dead sheep draped across its back. A man and woman squeeze together on a donkey, small child wedged between them. The market's parking lot collects animals dozing under shade, but the donkeys stand dejectedly in the sun. Goats and long-tailed sheep roam freely through the streets. Camels chew in figure-eights but spit and snarl if you get too close. The night is a nonstop chorus of braying donkeys, barking dogs, lizards that rustle and chirp, roosters crowing at 3 am, birds and insects. I won't be able to sleep in the quiet of Seattle ever again.

Nazra cooks over a charcoal fire dug into the sand in front of the cooking hut. She found peanuts (or "G" nuts, "Ground nuts" as they are called in Africa) in the market, shelled them and is now roasting them for us. She scoops sand onto a wok-like aluminum pan, heats the sand and drops in the peanuts. Once they are roasted, she sifts out the sand and leaves the peanuts on the screen to cool. Warm, salty and sand-gritty, they are delicious.

A pregnant patient comes to my ante natal clinic complaining of an eye infection. She had already seen the Traditional Healer who licked her eyeball. It didn't help. Another Traditional Healer had written the words of the Koran on a board, then washed the ink off with water and gave it to the woman to drink as a cure. She asks me for medication.

A string is tied around a painful limb. When someone has

pain, they cut her and let her bleed. One woman's abdomen is covered in scars and another in burns – also traditional medicine to treat pain. A jaundiced woman has been cut on the thumb side of her wrist to let out the bad blood. If there were leeches, I'm sure they would be used.

One of the nurse assistants asks me to attend to her sister in her home – a dried mud tukul with thatch roof. She is unmarried and pregnant. The Traditional Healer gave her herbs to end the pregnancy, but they destroyed her liver. Despite her ebony skin, she is yellow and wasted, and died two days later. Her shame at being pregnant and unmarried prevented her from coming to us for proper medications to safely end unwanted pregnancies. How do we get past such cultural barriers?

As our cleaner, Aziza's job is to wash clothes and dishes plus keep the compound clean and tidy. The hospital water-sanitation man cleans our latrine and shower daily with chlorine, but everything else is Aziza's responsibility. Even though our logistician built a brick and concrete sink for washing, Aziza prefers to sit on a hide-covered stool with 6 inch legs. She suds up clothes or dishes in a pan, then pours water over them from another pan to rinse. They dry in the sun on a rack made of chicken wire.

Every morning, Aziza sweeps the sand outside our tukuls. Gripping a handful of slim twigs, she bends from the waist and swings her arm side to side, side to side, side to side, whisking away leaves and debris that have fallen since the day before. This is all collected into a small pile outside our front gate and burned along with the community's garbage at dusk each night. Plastic bottles and bags, leaves, packaging and other debris burn in a toxic mix that fills our tired nostrils with acrid smoke and burns our eyes.

A child presents with measles. There are no medical records here. People are illiterate. Paper is destroyed by insects or crumbles to dust in the dry heat. We vaccinate siblings and the children living in nearby homes. A straw mat is unrolled under a shade tree. Raise the sleeve and jab into the grubby upper arm. No alcohol, no soap or cleaning of any kind. Flies and dust and snot and hot dirty kids. Most of them don't even cry. Their clothes are tied together with nylon string pulled from UN World Food Programme food sacks. I marvel at a hundred dinar note, worth a few inconsequential US pennies, stitched together with the same string.

Conversations are interesting around the table with two African men. Here's what I learned in my first month:

1. It's not unusual for boys to lose their virginity to animals. One technique is to dig a 2 ft x 2 ft pit to stand a donkey in so it can't get away.
2. Cow dung ash is a substitute for toothpaste.
3. Blow into a cow's vagina to increase milk production.
4. Use cow urine mixed with dung ash to bleach your hair.
5. Use cow urine to separate the heavy cream and make sour cream.

With no artificial light, the stars in the night sky are so close; you can reach out and touch them with your fingertips. Vivid. Sharp. Gorgeous. That is, once the haze of dust and smoke has lifted. If you look at the sand and the straw roofs in the moonlight, you can almost imagine snow, except it's 80 degrees at 10 pm. The moon is so bright, you can walk easily in the nighttime.

One day on patient rounds, I become suspicious when every blood pressure is "one hundred over sixty." I ask a nurse assistant to take a patient's pulse. She grips his forearm, stares at her own wrist and pronounces "sixty." She has no watch. Our "nursing staff" have had no training prior to our team's arrival, so there is a lot to teach. But they are kind and hard-working and want to help their community.

A Traditional Birth Attendant worked in the antenatal clinic twice a week for a month. I was puzzled as to why I was estimating dates so differently from her. I was new at this, and she'd delivered dozens and dozens of babies. I checked and double checked: Fundus (top of the uterus) at the belly button = 20 weeks. One finger breadth below the belly button = minus two weeks per finger. One finger breadth above the belly button = plus one week per finger. I called out "30 weeks" and she said "24." My "16" was met by her "28." I realized she can't do numbers; she can't subtract four from twenty or add ten to twenty. I made a chart for the wall of the numbers 1 to 40 in both English and Arabic. Smiling and pointing to the numbers, she shook her head. She can't read Arabic. So I wrote out the Arabic pronunciation as my guide and am teaching her math.

Everyone wants to learn, but the danger is in assuming they know more than they do.

Midway

Unfamiliar with desert climates, I was completely caught off guard with a cold snap in January. National staff wore heavy coats and I wore every t-shirt and pair of socks I brought. We all bundled under multiple blankets at night. I complained to friends on email and my friend Sheila promised to send me warm clothing.

The doctor, a translator and I respond to a report of "Whooping Cough" at one of the village schools. A fence of grass bundles surrounds a large earth square where hundreds of children gather in front of the headmaster. The assembly scatters like a leaf in the wind once our presence became a distraction.

Like the Big Bad Wolf, I thought, "I could blow down the school room structures with one big breath." Woven straw mats were fashioned into walls and roofs, held together with twine.

We select a classroom at random. Ninety-seven boys age 8-10 sit on grass mats in their bare feet, shoes stowed on the roof above the doorway. There are no chairs or desks, only a well-worn chalkboard in front. The boys sing us a song, and we ask who has a cough. Two boys stand and push out dry coughs. The doctor examines them with a smile. Three more stand and try to cough. The doctor pats and listens. More and more pop up and soon a chorus of thirty young boys cough for our attention.

There was no Whoop.

Fatima, one of our community health workers, invites us to her tukul for a visit. There is one large wood-framed bed with a draping mosquito net. The packed dirt floor still shows scratch marks from earlier sweeping. Kitchen pots and various utensils are neatly stacked in one corner along with a battery operated boom-box. Her long fabric covers hang in a vibrant color collage along a rod swinging from the thatch ceiling.

We are seated on the bed and spritzed three times with clinging perfume that competes with sandalwood incense. Sandalwood oil is daubed on the throat and under the nose. The pungent scents cover gagging body odor in a land where bathing with precious water is a luxury few can afford.

Her sister pours water over our hands from a plastic pitcher, and they dry instantly in the heat. She serves tiny glasses of hot sweet tea from a metal tray along with a dried date. We pass around a small bowl of sugar with toasted sesame seeds. In order to not "double dip," the technique is to scoop a half spoonful and toss it into your mouth. It tastes surprisingly delicious.

Next comes a communal bowl of sorghum, pounded for hours and boiled to make it somewhat palatable. Making a spoon of index and middle fingers, I scoop up a small amount, dragging it through a slimy green okra sauce. It is flavorless and gritty. The sister once again pours water over our hands and brings us cool bottles of sparkling apple juice from the market.

I'm starting to get a bit uneasy at Habila being the only quiet place in Darfur. People are moving more and more in this direction because it's safe. There is room to graze animals and word has spread of the relative calm. More people = more problems = more violence = more displaced = more needs.

Being tall, I see things in high, hard to reach places. Often this translates to giant spiders and pigeon feathers, but one afternoon I spy tins of cream on the top kitchen shelf. Everyone on our small team drinks black coffee and tea, so these had been pushed to the back as unnecessary along with milk powder. On tippy toes, I also discover strawberry flavored Nestle's Quik. I stir the three ingredients into a metal bowl and place it in the freezer of our gas powered fridge. Every couple hours, I scrape the sides with a fork and by dinnertime, it is ice cream! I hadn't told the others, in case it was a disaster.

Darfur is dry in the sense of "hot and arid" as well as "no alcohol." Happy Hour for us was simply a time to drink water together in the shade of our compound tree and digest the day. No one anticipated a Strawberry Nestle's Quik Ice Cream Happy Hour.

Nazra and Aziza rush over when they heard squeals, and stare with puzzled faces as we dip spoonfuls into each other's mouths. I offer each a spoon. Nazra's face explodes in surprise as she tentatively touches her tongue to the cold pinkness. Aziza spits it to the ground, shaking her head and backing away. It probably didn't help having us laugh at her reaction, but the following day, she comes to work with a long scarf wound around her neck and pretends to be hoarse. Neither had ever tasted something cold before.

Strawberry Nestle's Quik is soon joined by key lime (little green lemons were available locally), mango (in season), chocolate (also Nestle's Quik), peanut butter and coffee (Nescafe). I teach Nazra how to make it, and she joins us each evening before going home.

When my replacement arrives, part of our handover is Ice Cream Making. Habila Happy Hour Ice Cream has become legend, and was noted on my End of Mission Evaluation once I arrived in Geneva for debriefing.

Another death last night. We have one about every second day. They seek us out when it's too late to help. About 1 am a comatose ten year old boy comes cradled in his father's arms. He dies an hour later from probable Hepatitis. It's sad and takes a lot out of us. Pregnant women die bleeding. Children die from malaria and meningitis. Gunshot wounds and stabbings, we can't save. Babies die in childbirth and sometimes their mothers as well. Sometimes you can convince yourself it isn't as bad as it really is.

In the quiet hours I ruminate a lot about my worth, my impact, my tangible contributions here. I don't feel them yet. What have I done other than be amazed?

One day I ask the water boy, what is the sad brown donkey's name?

Blank stare.

I tapped my chest "Sue." And tapped his chest "Adam." Then pointed to the donkey, "Him?"

"Humar." "Donkey" in Arabic.

"Yes, I understand he's a donkey but what is his name?"

"Humar."

"I'll call him 'Bob.'" Adam just looks at me as I laugh.

Bats swoop and swarm at dusk, like the flock of crows at home that head to their roost at dusk. I can't remember if bats carry rabies.

It's my job to create a birthing program. Anyone who knows ER medical staff knows the only thing in the universe that makes our hearts race is the phrase, "Her water broke, and she needs to push!" I clear a small two room storage space and have logistics repair an old rusted delivery table. In the front room, I conduct Ante Natal Clinic two days a week. All the pregnant mothers are weighed and checked for baby's position and movement, any signs of infection, and are given pre-natal vitamins and tetanus immunizations. In the last trimester we also give each mother a mosquito net and encourage her to come to our facility for the birth. Only a few take us up on the offer of free care.

Most deliveries happen in the home with a Traditional Birth Attendant – usually a woman from the community with some experience in births. The in-home deliveries are "dirty" – without soap or running water. The cord is cut with a kitchen knife and rubbed in the dirt to stop the bleeding. So many newborns die that the tradition is to not name them for forty days.

If you ever think anything is private, unknown or sacred on a mission, think again. One day, our cook Nazra comes into my room pretending to dust. Dusting was not her job nor was there any work-related reason for her to be in my room, but I see her eyes dart to the zip lock baggie and wait for what was to come.

She gestures at the condom-filled baggie with raised eyebrows and tips her head in a classic "What's this?" pose.

Nazra spoke no English. I spoke no Arabic.

I open the baggie, pull out a foil packet and hand it to her. She flips her hand palm-side up and shrugs her chin. "What's this?"

"Condom."

Again, the palm flips up.

I make a rounded hand sweep away from my abdomen indicating pregnancy, then shake my finger and head "NO!"

Nazra's eyebrows shoot up. "No?" Shoulders shrug with both hands raised, palms up: "How?"

I hang my hand in front of my groin and raise my index finger to mimic an erection. Then I tear open the foil and roll the condom onto my finger. Nazra's mouth hangs slightly open as she studies my movements.

"Understand?"

Nodding, she holds out her hand.

"You want?" I nod toward the baggie.

Again, she holds out her hand. I give her two.

She stands looking at the two condoms on her palm for a moment, then motions toward me with eyes on the baggie. "More."

I give her the baggie. She smiles, turns and leaves my room.

Despite the best laid plans and Mefloquine, it seems my last three days of groaning and writhing in bed with horrid wrenching body aches and hallucinations was malaria. Last night, I didn't know how I could walk the twenty steps to the latrine, much less squat to pee and get up again. Rolling over in bed was agony. I didn't realize I had a fever, but wasn't thinking too clearly. I thought Rob Thomas was in my room singing to me.

All I could dream of was a hot shower, glass of Jack Daniels and soft feather bed at home. Instead I had a cold shower, cup of herbal tea and what passes for a bed here – lumpy mattress atop a stretchy nylon sling on a metal frame, gauzily covered by a mosquito net.

The body aches are mostly gone now but my head isn't so clear. I was doing pretty well until I realized, dripping inside the shower room, that I hadn't taken a towel with me. Maybe it's best to just go back to bed.

End of Mission

Bob has been replaced. I saw him limping a couple days ago and now there is a younger, slimmer donkey to bring our water.

"There's a baby in the street!" Zenab rushed to our compound on her way to work the night shift. The newborn lying in the sand looked to be only a couple hours old. We scooped him up in a towel and ran to the hospital to wash and warm him. From nowhere, more and more staff arrived with baby clothes, but Zenab held a tight grip and took him home in the morning.

Speculation was the baby was "illegal" meaning conceived out of wedlock consensually or most likely - not. If the mother were found, she would be imprisoned, beaten or worse. A woman in another village is currently on trial for Attempted Murder for abandoning her baby. In a nearby town when a baby was found hidden in a well, the authorities rounded up all the newly delivered mothers to question them, demanding to see their babies. Women in Sudan have fewer rights than a donkey. A Sudanese man told me, "All women want babies, so it doesn't matter if she becomes pregnant after rape."

Our week was Saturday to Friday, which made reporting to a European office structure interesting. Nazra and Aziza had Fridays off, the Muslim holy day like the western Sunday. Fridays were also the expat's day off, unless emergencies arose at the hospital. It was a day of lounging and sloth, of movie watching and reading. We also made our own meals.

I'd brought a small packet of Italian Seasoning and decided to make spaghetti and meatballs for our small team. I'd asked Nazra to buy me some "meat" in the market. "Meat" would not necessarily be beef, rather, whatever animal had been recently slaughtered. As I looked at the unfamiliar chunk of flesh on the table, I was unsure whether it was cow, camel or some other creature. In any case, this was the basis of my sauce, and I sliced it into small pieces.

I clamped the aluminum grinder to a table edge. Piece by piece, I fed the mystery meat into the top and circled the handle. But the strings and gristle clogged the small extruder holes, and every few minutes I had to disassemble the grinder to clear the obstruction. The sun had begun to beat down and the ground meat exercise had me wet with sweat.

Next came making sauce. No cans – only small, hard local tomatoes and onions from the market. In the 130 degree heat, I blanched and stripped skins from the tomatoes and chopped onions until tears mixed with sweat. Finally, the ingredients were ready to combine and stew over the charcoal fire.

A nomad group invites us to join them for a day. While the men sit under a tree and drink sweet tea, we women laugh, blow up balloons for the children, braid hair and cook a goat they'd slaughtered … all without sharing a common language. I start a game of baseball with the kids, using a stick and chunk of dried dung. The men bring a camel, and we take turns riding. I thought I would fall off as the beast lurches to stand. The proper method is to hold onto the saddle horn front and back and cross your legs across its neck.

Gingerly dismounting, the women approach me, "Now we want to go in your car." The experience for them is the equivalent of us riding their camel. Twenty-five pile into my Land Cruiser. At first, most are scared and want to stop after about a hundred yards. Then one woman points and wants to go THERE. Another points THERE. Go to that tent. Go around that one. And honk. They ululate and sing with happiness. When the ride is finished, they can't figure out how to open the door and the laughter starts again.

A perfect day.

Sheila's care package arrives, hand carried by my replacement. Inside is a pair of long johns.

It's been an interesting ride, this first MSF mission. What will I tell in my debriefing? Of the frustrations? Of the dedication and incredibly hard work by all to provide good medical care to these people? Of feeling lost and alone, unprepared? Or of personal and professional growth?

What do I tell them about the future? Will I do this again? Is this really what I want to do? At nearly 50, can I do it? I miss home and friends but itch to travel and experience more than the small world I inhabit.

I look at the honors I've had these six months: being welcomed into homes, into lives, into the most intimate moments. I've delivered babies and watched them die. I've evaluated for diseases I've never seen before. I've built buildings and teaching programs and implemented lifesaving procedures. I know the work I've done has touched hundreds of lives, just as my life has been touched by theirs.

I had Janjaweed offer me my own tent and camel if I come to live with them. I learned about Islam and a smattering of Arabic. I learned about malnutrition and how to palpate a pregnant abdomen. I had conversations by gesture about sex and condoms.

I made ice cream in the desert.

The Red Zone

It's wet hot. Hot like you've never felt it. Weakness-inducing hot. Lethargy-producing hot. Dry mouth hot. And it's about to get hotter still.

Day after day, three or four times in a twelve hour shift, my pre Red Zone ritual is the same. With a wad of toilet paper tucked into the hip pocket of my green scrub pants, I walk across the jagged broken-rock plaza in sloppy, ill-fitting white gumboots that make my feet twist and slip. Baking under the Sierra Leonean sun, a rough brick structure hosts the latrine. A white vinyl tarp with a dark blue stripe separates men on one side and women on the other in our most private of moments. I step onto the three foot by three foot grey plastic latrine cover, lift the handle of the hole-covering lid and carefully squat over the keyhole-shaped opening known as a "drop hole." The toilet paper is already damp from sweat, but accomplishes its purpose. I dance and jiggle to pull up my scrubs.

Outside the doorway, I pause to wash my hands; not with soap, but with chlorine solution. Eau de Chlorine, Ebola-killing chlorine, the ever-present perfume of this mission. 50 liter white containers sport a tap and sit atop a sturdy wooden table, chlorinated water splashing down onto those sharp rocks. Wash stations live at every entrance to every activity. They greet us at the outside entrance to the Treatment Center where a watchman sprays our shoes and takes our temperature by pointing a plastic gun at our temples. The chlorine has already whitened the bottoms of my jeans and holes have begun to form. Wash stations stand guard at the entry to changing rooms and the canvas tents we work inside. Wash stations beckon us as we move from area to area within the compound. "When in doubt, wash your hands." Chlorine is our comfort and protector.

Back in the canvas administrative tent, I grab two half-liter plastic bags of water, rinse them with chlorine and bite a hole in one corner. I open my throat, squeeze my fist and swallow the water in a single gulp. And a second bag. It's a fine balance. Two things I don't want to do inside The Red Zone: urinate or faint from dehydration.

My partners and I review treatment plans for each of our Intensive Care patients, collect up medications, fluids and supplies and divide duties. No one may enter The Red Zone without a buddy to make sure there are no breaches or exposures. We literally watch each other's backs. I ask an expat nurse to oversee our actions from outside the ten foot high Plexiglas walls.

Three national nurses and I tromp across the jagged stones, greeting the water-sanitation crew, the social workers, the volunteers and doctors. No touch. No contact. No handshakes. No "high five." Not even a tapping of elbows like in a Cholera intervention. In a physically demonstrative culture like this, we repeatedly remind the local staff "No Touch Policy."

We wash our hands with chlorine again at the entrance to the donning area under the watchful gaze of an attendant whose job is to be sure we follow every detail of the protocol. We each gather seven things: vinyl unsterile gloves, sterile gloves, apron, duck-bill mask, hood, goggles and the one piece impermeable yellow coverall. Anything in pockets must be removed. The poke of a stray pen can expose you to this most deadly of infections. I search for Baby Powder – without a dusting, sweaty hands cannot struggle into the first pair of gloves.

Wooden benches line the walls of the tent and mirrors hang every six to eight feet. Sitting on a bench, I begin to gently tug my suit over the gumboots, careful to not tear the impervious fabric. The loops at the end of the arms wrap around my thumbs to keep the sleeves from riding up. The orange duck bill mask muffles my words and pokes through a slash I've torn through the face-covering hood. I ease the hood down to my eyebrows and tie it in three places behind my head. I squeeze the metal nose-grip of the mask against the dark bags under my eyes.

Sweat droplets tickle down my neck and back, soaking my scrubs. I work the second pair of medical gloves over the vinyl pair, and gently pull them up my forearm to encompass the suit at my wrists. The attendant hands me goggles which have been sprayed with anti-fog and ties my thick vinyl butcher apron behind my back, assuring the release tie hangs near my right hip. He then writes my name on the forehead of my hood and inspects the goggles to be sure no skin is left exposed. When my coworkers are similarly prepped, the attendant marks the time on our PPE (Personal Protective Equipment) covered arms, and the clock begins to tick. We have one hour to do our work.

We push through the one way gate into The Red Zone.

Clomping through the crunchy rocks, we first check Triage for patients who wait to be escorted to their room in the Suspect Area. We wave and call out positive encouragement to patients waiting for test results. Even in this, Doctors Without Borders' newest and best treatment facility, only half will survive Ebola.

We enter the ICU – a huge tent with a concrete floor and twenty-four beds: twelve on each side and a Plexiglas alley from the outside, up the middle to the center of the tent. Inside that alleyway walks the expat nurse, supervising us, watching for breaches in our PPE, retrieving things we need for patient care and pushing them on a six foot table slanted downwards. Everything goes one way – always in and never out. Once, a nurse took a patient chart "inside," and there it had to stay. The solution was for her to hold the chart against the plexiglas wall while on the "outside" I took pictures with my cell phone, page by page. She then sat for an hour recreating it by hand.

Although not an "Intensive Care Unit" in the conventional sense of ventilators and cardiac monitors, these patients are incredibly fragile, combative, comatose, oozing diarrhea and blood. They require the heaviest care and closest attention. We encourage fluids – an orange-flavored version of ORS (Oral Rehydration Salts) – sip by sip by sip. Many are unable to keep down oral fluids and we move to IVs: six liters a day. But IVs are tricky; tape slips off sweaty arms and IVs fall out. Momo, a nineteen year old boy, confused and disoriented by the disease, regularly wobbled upright at his cot-side, disconnected the IV tubing, aimed the lifesaving fluid at the urine bucket, and reconnected the tubing once the bag was empty. He thought the fluid was poison.

Today I try to start an IV on a six year old girl who spent two days in a government holding center prior to transfer to our facility. She is so severely dehydrated, her lips are bleeding and she barely has a pulse. I bend over her arm and drops of sweat swim on the lens of my goggles. I tip my head this way and that, encouraging the drops to roll out of my field of vision. My buddy says, "I don't like your goggles. Go out."

These words are not given or taken lightly, nor is there any further discussion. Any breach in protocol can endanger your own life and that of everyone on the team. Everyone has the authority to evict anyone they feel is in danger.

I leave my supplies for the next nurse to try for an IV on this girl. She dies before the next team enters an hour later.

Soaked in sweat, body temperature unmeasurably high, we clomp to a doffing station. I wait until the person in front of me finishes – the longest ten minutes of my life, unable to sit for fear of tearing the suit, unable to drink or wipe the sweat from my face. Waiting. Hot and miserable and woozy and thirsty. Waiting to begin the crucial final step. Ebola might have snuck onto my suit, unseen, unnoticed in the form of droplets. There is no room for the smallest of errors in undressing.

Finally it is my turn, and I dance onto the concrete platform. First, wash hands wearing two layers of gloves, in the chlorine hand wash. Next, pull that right hip string to loosen the apron, duck my head and drop it off into a plastic garbage can filled with a tenfold concentration of chlorine. Dip three times and toss into a second grey can. Now comes the most blessed of feelings. Better than Christmas morning. Better than ice cream or your favorite song. The attendant pumps five times to pressurize the chlorine sprayer, and you spread your arms wide as if to fly.

The chlorine water sprayed onto my suit is the most fantastic sensation ever known on earth. My body sighs as the cooling spray hits my PPE top to bottom, front to back and all sides in between. I could hug the attendant but she is on the "clean" side and I'm still "dirty." I simply tell her, "Thank you."

She continues to direct me in each step of doffing, although I've done this dozens of times. No room for error. Next remove the hood. Wash your hands. Now take off the outer gloves. Wash your hands. Now look in the mirror to unzip your suit, turning it inside out and only touching the inside. Pull it down to your knees and use your boots to step on it and pull it off. Take it by the inside and toss it into the red-lined garbage can. Wash your hands. Close your eyes and take off your goggles. Dunk three times and toss in to soak with the apron. Wash your hands. Close your eyes and take off your mask. Toss into the red-lined garbage can. Wash your hands. Take off your second pair of gloves. Wash your hands.

Now step near the edge of the platform for the attendant to spray your boots. Twist to the left and then right in what we call the Michael Jackson Move. Now, raise your sole to be sprayed and step into the "clean." Repeat with your other foot and you're finished!

The attendant hands me a bag of water which I rinse under chlorine, bite the corner and gulp. I scrub my face with clean water and soap. This feels like heaven. I grab another bag and head for the administrative tent to chart our care and debrief with the doctors. Fans blow hot air across my sweat.

I drink two more bags of water before my heart stops pounding.

They Are There

"Are we going to see lions?"

"They are there," the park guide answered in the typical ambiguous Ugandan way.

Our team had chosen a weekend retreat to Murchinson Falls Park, a glorious game sanctuary a few hours southwest of Gulu, where we provided medical care in huge displacement camps. This lush park, rich with natural beauty, was only twenty-five miles from the abject misery of tens of thousands of people and their daily struggle for survival. Such breaks don't come without guilt. Humanitarian work can be grueling, and you must "put on your own oxygen mask before helping others." The ongoing stories of terror and torture by the anti-government rebel Lord's Resistance Army (LRA) had left our hearts heavy and exhausted.

In this protective environment, wildlife thrived. Crocodiles lined the riverbank, mouths smiling open in the sunshine as birds picked debris from between sharp teeth. Hundreds of immersed hippos hid their massive bulk, poking only nostrils and blinking eyes out of the water. White ibis rode the backs of droopy-horned Cape buffalo caked in dried mud. A mother elephant, ears flapping and trunk waving, charged into the river, trumpeting a shrill warning as she guided her babies away from our uplifted cameras.

My thoughts drifted to other mothers, those who had lost their children to the LRA. The displacement camps across northern Uganda were ostensibly set up as "protective zones" for civilians, but in reality were more akin to concentration camps than to the natural ebb and flow of home and family life. Even in these "safe zones" the LRA poached children.

"Will we see lions?" I asked again.

"They are there."

In a way, the history of Murchison is the history of northern Uganda's Acholi people. Winston Churchill referred to Uganda as "the pearl of Africa," and by the 1960's, it was considered the best wildlife refuge in all of East Africa: overflowing with elephants, rhinos, antelope, monkeys and all the creatures that sparked our imaginations in National Geographic magazine. But mounting political upheaval created a hunger for ivory to fund clashing armies. Elephants and rhinos were the first herds to be decimated. In the 1970's Idi Amin's army fed on the wild beasts. By the 1980's, expanding guerilla armies hunted many species to extinction to feed their appetite for war.

Oddly enough, the LRA is deplorably responsible for the resurgence of the wild game population of Murchison Park. Poachers didn't dare enter, fearing attacks from the brutal gang that intermittently hides inside the vast expanse. Ironically, 1.8 million indigenous Acholis remain trapped, listless and dying in nearby camps, while dik dik, hyenas and giraffes run free.

As a member of a rival northern tribe, Idi Amin oppressed the Acholi population when he seized power in 1971. Okello (an Acholi) overthrew Amin in 1979 and was in turn toppled in 1986 by still-to-this-day-president-for-life Museveni. As soon as he took control of the government, President Museveni began a campaign of retaliation against ethnic northern groups. Cycles of revenge killings have plagued northern Uganda for generations.

Alice Lakwena, with claims to have channeled the Holy Spirit, armed her anti-government group with rocks and sticks and smeared their bodies with magic oil that would "melt enemy bullets." Another charismatic Acholi, Joseph Kony – also claiming to be possessed by spirits - gathered a rebel band that would blanket the north with fear and paranoia. For the next twenty years, Kony's inappropriately named Lord's Resistance Army abducted over twenty five thousand children and terrorized millions in Uganda, South Sudan, Congo and Central African Republic. Experts estimate under two hundred combatants remain in Kony's ragtag army, yet so horrendous were their atrocities, those stories keep the rarely seen LRA alive.

"Have you seen any LRA?"

"They are there."

From behind, Joyce looks like any other poor Ugandan child. An ill-fitting yellow dress hangs a couple sizes too big. "She'll grow into it." She clutches a brown stuffed bear in one hand and sips from a Coca Cola bottle in the other. She hovers in the doorway of the hospital ward but won't wander away. This has been her home for the last six months.

When Joyce turns around, you see her story. Her face, arms

and legs are a patchwork of black and pink skin grafts. Tufts of hair dot her pink scalp.

What possesses young men to attack a van filled with people on their way to work, or to visit family, or off to a market to buy food for supper? If there were a motive, perhaps robbery, it would be easier to understand. But the overflowing van, with baby Joyce and her mother squeezed in, was not attacked by bandits. They were attacked by the LRA using fear as their weapon of choice. The van was riddled with bullets. Those who didn't die immediately were bludgeoned to death with metal pipes. Their screams muffled into moans, and the only sound was the heavy breathing of the blood splattered teens standing over the bodies.

Then Joyce cried. Clutching her still-warm mother, she reached out to the boys. She clung to their arms, seeking a brother's comfort. They carried her to a dry patch of grass at the side of the road, and set it on fire.

Did she wiggle away while the boys were ransacking the van? Or did the fire burn past her? I imagine the shock when the charred, whimpering child was found by a passerby.

I met Joyce at Lacor Hospital in Gulu on her second birthday. There was no party. No cake or ice cream. No pink balloon-filled celebration. Instead she was examined by an international plastic surgery team. She would need several surgeries to free the contractures on her right arm and repair scar tissue on her face and neck. On occasion, a small smile tickled the corners of her mouth, but most of her days were spent clutching her ragged teddy bear.

Yet Joyce was only one of thousands of stories. For well over a decade, ninety percent of the population of Acholiland lived in government sponsored "protection" camps. Twenty to thirty thousand individuals per camp – real people with names and families – living in mud tukuls side by side, row after row, straw roofs providing slivers of shade from the unrelenting sun. There is no work, only waiting for the World Food Programme to deliver oil, soy-cornmeal meal and a little salt each month.

Even in these camps, lacking nutritious food to eat, dying at astonishingly high rates from HIV/AIDS, lacking the most basic of services, people brew vast quantities of body- and mind-numbing alcohol. With ambitions dulled, people settled into a mundane way of life. Domestic abuse soared and arbitrators were as drunk as participants. Children heard every sound from the next tukul five feet away. Violence was rampant. Militias formed to protect the camp population, but soon the militia were raping and beating with impunity. Time and time again, protectors become perpetrators. A few desperate women were brave enough to farm in groups just beyond the borders of the camps.

But they were there.

As a member of the Doctors Without Borders (MSF) team, I tended to the children sent to Lacor Hospital from the internally displaced persons camps. Little acts of mercy made a dent in the injustices suffered. Balloons for the kids. Some coins to help mothers pay for a seat on a transport van to Gulu Town and food in the hospital. Our camp medical team would follow the children after discharge, but many were too far into their illnesses. Debilitated from chronic malnutrition or diarrhea, often they did not make it "home" to the camps.

We were notified that an international plastic surgery organization was coming to provide free reconstructive surgery for LRA victims. My role was to examine and interview twenty disfigured people. Their stories were told matter-of-factly, lack of emotion belied by an occasional escaped tear. Each story was more horrifying than the one before.

Mary was grabbed while harvesting cassava. She was raped for three unrelenting days, then offered a choice: she could be beaten to death, have her lips cut off or her hand chopped off. What bravery she must have exhibited as she held on to the branch with her left hand while the machete came down.

Okello John needed his hands. He chose to lose both ears.

Young Richard had one eye missing and was covered in scars. He was working the soil to prepare for planting when his hoe came down on a crude bomb. His two sons were killed.

Adam had been riding his bicycle to church when he was grabbed, beaten and stripped naked. A rifle was shoved into his mouth and discharged. He was left for dead. Crude surgery left a puckered hole in his cheek, exposing teeth in a permanent grimace. He covered his face when he ate.

One after another, young and old, with amputated lips, ears or hands, men and women told their stories. I felt helpless. There was little any surgical team could do. Skin grafts. Some cosmetic improvements. I wanted to undo their scars. I wanted to restore them to "before." I told myself that the best way of helping was to listen. By absorbing their stories, I might be able to understand the visceral fear that keeps people huddled in miserable camps for decades instead of returning to their lush homelands. I could speak out on their behalf and give wider voice to their stories.

I carried these people with me when I went on a mid-mission break to Geneva for a security training course. It was impossible not to compare the two lifestyles.

The worst thing about Geneva was the cigarette smoke, choking and clinging to skin, hair and clothes. The best thing was a week free from itchy biting insects.

In Uganda: 25 cents for "meat on a stick." Geneva: $30 for a steak.

In Uganda: carrying everything from 20 liters of water to a stick of sugar cane on your head. Geneva: in your car.

In Uganda: stewed "edible rat" served over ugali. Geneva: everything except rodents.

In Uganda: cold water bucket showers under the stars. Geneva: long hot showers with miniature scented soaps.

In Uganda: Dinner at an outdoor "pork joint" with vultures lurking for dropped bits. Geneva: Bars with vultures lurking for dropped hints.

In Uganda: Waragi (a hooch made from sugar cane that can make you blind) in a little plastic pouch. Geneva: fine wine in a crystal glass.

In Uganda: lighting storms and dumps of warm rain. Geneva: glooming overcast Seattle-like skies.

In Geneva children attend school and sleep in their beds each night.

In Uganda: night commuters.

At nine, Patrick was a night commuter. He and several other orphans lived with a kind woman he called his aunty in Awere camp eight miles outside Gulu Town. His father disappeared when he was little, shortly before his mother died from AIDS. His aunt's round tukul was small, only ten feet in diameter. It was constructed of sun-dried bricks made of straw and mud. She did her best to make the small space home, decorating the smooth walls by dipping the children's hands in ash and pressing them into the still wet clay.

"These are our Happy Hands," she told him.

Every evening, as the sun began to slip, Patrick and other children emerged from the camps and converged on unpaved roads. Little ones were carried by older children or rode on the center bar of bicycles. Waves of such night commuters made their nightly trek into Gulu. Forty thousand children slept in bus terminals, churches and unoccupied buildings, curling into each other for warmth. With the dawn, they walked to school and then "home" to the camps, returning to Gulu again at dusk.

Children night commute for many reasons, the main being the deep-rooted fear of the LRA, moving like ghosts in the dark. Others leave because of family breakdown; parents emotionally and physically unavailable for so many reasons (personal atrocities, illness from HIV/AIDS, dead or abandoned spouses, alcohol, rape, beatings). Children cling to each other for support.

But the journey itself wasn't without risk. Men in military dress detour school age girls behind bushes. Boys return home with bruises and fractured limbs. Some don't arrive home at all.

Patrick's aunt must have spent the day watching the dusty

road. One morning passed. Then another. There was nothing she could do. He was gone.

Patrick was in fourth grade when he was abducted. Instead of learning to read, he was surviving the most brutal of conditions. I met him after he'd escaped. He wouldn't look up while talking about his ordeal. There was no emotion in his soft voice as he spoke of beatings and threats to kill or be killed. Biting a woman to death, bludgeoning other children, rape, sneaking back into camps to steal and kill anyone who tried to interfere. He was given plants to eat that made him hallucinate and alcohol to blunt his resistance. Eventually he stopped thinking about the Happy Hands on the wall of his aunty's tukul and did what he needed to survive.

Yet Patrick was one of the lucky ones; he'd escaped. He wouldn't tell me how, just that he'd gained a position of trust and took advantage of the freedom it offered. He never said how many people he had killed. And I didn't ask.

In January 2006, we heard of an unprecedented move: the United Nations mounted a covert operation to capture Joseph Kony. A squad of American-trained Guatemalan Special Ops troops, equipped with M-16s and the latest technology, were no match for the child warriors. More Guatemalans than LRA died. Three months later, Kony joined international talks with no intention of signing any peace agreement that didn't guarantee his immunity from prosecution. The talks achieved nothing; the LRA continued their raids.

By 2009 all but two of the displacement camps were closed and eighty percent of the population reoccupied their homelands or moved to Gulu. Night commuters no longer make their twilight trek for safety. Gulu was granted city status with a population over 150,000. Mud brick and thatch have given way to concrete buildings with iron sheeting roofs. Businessmen once banished to India have returned to occupy the town center. New bank branches boast ATMs, and four hospitals have replaced camp clinics. The city still lacks infrastructure, but is abuzz with energy. Streets once used only by herds of long-horned cows and NGO white Toyota Land Cruisers are now clogged with motor scooters and beat up sedans.

In 2011 U.S. military special ops forces permanently deployed to northern Uganda, pushing Kony's base west to Congo's Garamba National Park. His final lifeline is the ivory trade, and scores of rangers have been killed defending the elephant population. Ivory tusks from the magnificent creatures are smuggled to Port Sudan, Kenya and Tanzania and then to Asia; the profits buy more uniforms and ammunition. 20,000 elephants in the 1960's have dwindled to 2000 today.

By massacring the elephants and destroying the park habitat, the LRA have destroyed themselves. Only about one hundred and twenty LRA fighters remain, accompanied by a few dozen women and their children. Defectors are arrested despite their young age. Kidnapped as children, sleeping soundly in their beds, they now face adult consequences for their actions. Kony hasn't been seen in years.

Sporadic attacks continue into South Sudan and Central African Republic, each time reigniting fears of past terror. Even after months of relative quiet, one LRA raid halts rural farming and fields lie fallow for the season. Traders, governmental officials and aid workers avoid travel to "no go" areas, leaving the population without essential goods or services. The fear of fear becomes the reality of fear.

I did see them in Murchison Park. They were there. Sitting in the shade of an Acacia tree. Rolling in mock play. Shadows blended in the tall sand-colored grass. The birds fell silent. Movement in the corner of my eye, too fast to capture on camera. At least I think so. I think they were there.

Snap Judgment

The UN plane disappeared through rapidly gathering storm clouds. The engine grew faint, then silent. I shrugged the backpack off my drooping shoulders and watched it sink into the mud. I no longer cared. It held only the necessities; luxury items like soap and toothpaste were left behind for the new nurse. It was her turn to save this little corner of the world. I had nothing more to give. My plan was to fly to Juba for a desperately needed shower and a bed with an actual mattress and sheets, then to Geneva for end of mission debriefing, and finally home to my cozy little nest in Seattle.

But I wasn't on the list.

"If you're not on the list," the pilot said, "you don't get on the plane."

The lone passenger on the eighteen-seat plane tried to pass his mobile phone over the hulking shoulder of the pilot, who waved a tattered paper in the air. For all I knew the paper could be his shopping list. I pleaded, yelled then sobbed but the click and whir of the propellers drowned me out. The armor which had sustained me over this six month mission – discipline, confidence, compassion - melted. The pilot hesitated for a moment but snapped the window closed. The passenger shook his head sadly. I watched in disbelief as the plane bumped down the potholed airstrip. I slumped to the ground and sobbed into my hands.

This was my fifth mission trip to Africa, my second to Sudan with Medicines Sans Frontiers (or to Americans, Doctors Without Borders). My team of 10 logisticians and medicals spent most of the previous five frustrating months responding to conflicts and epidemic outbreaks and wild goose chases across southern Sudan while the decades-long civil war raged against the north. With virtually no infrastructure, diseases like cholera, measles and meningitis were rampant. Our job was to contain such outbreaks with the expertise of MSF. But five months is a long time to spend bouncing along unpaved roads and sleeping on straw mats in mud tukuls, and I was beyond weary.

I was looking forward to attending a weeklong conference in Geneva when the civil war crashed into Abyei town. For years MSF ran a hospital serving the Dinka tribe who occupied the four thousand square mile expanse of desert along an ill-defined border with hopefully-soon-to-be-independent South Sudan. Economically desirable with its rich oil reserves, the Abyei Region had longstanding and conflicting ethnic, cultural and linguistic claims.

Tensions had flared at a military checkpoint then boiled over into the town. The market, a hive of commerce under the shade of straw roofs, burned to the ground. Soldiers forced their way into the hospital to finish the fight. Bullets hit walls and patients scattered. When MSF staff demanded they leave with their weapons, they torched the hospital and shot at the fleeing staff.

One nurse was killed and several more wounded. The only exit was under fire on a UN helicopter.

The world of Abyei burst into flames. Thirty thousand civilians ran, only stopping to grab their children. They fled south across the river to Agok, very biblical Book of Revelations-sounding, but really only a bend in the road.

"Shall we go to Geneva or Agok?" my Head of Mission asked with a wink. Agok was the answer, but not without wistful thoughts of comfort and safety in Geneva.

On our arrival, Agok's makeshift airstrip was muddy from recent downpours. The landing gear ground in deep, causing our plane come to an abrupt stop. Instantly we were surrounded by jumping children, pointing fingers at us, cheeping like little birds, "Hawaja! Hawaja! Hawaja!" The flock of children excitedly pulled us to a white wall surrounding the Catholic hospital. Inside were several thatched roof structures and a one story, non-descript medical building. The appearance of the compound didn't cause any alarm, but the cluster of Kenyan priests and nuns, huddled together with rucksacks in hand, did. They gestured frantically as we approached.

"We will go now," said a portly man with a deeply furrowed brow and wooden cross hanging around his neck, handing over a large ring of keys. "We will leave on your plane." With our supplies soaking in the rain, the priest made a hurried sign of the cross, and with a "God be with you," boarded his brood and flew away.

The fighting began in the gap between night and morning, a booming in the distance. I lay inside a mosquito net on a too-short cot in a storage room, trying to calm my overactive brain. When you wake to the first wave of shots, you wonder, *Was that gunfire or a clap of thunder?* With the second blast, you move.

I rolled onto the floor holding my breath, and tried to listen beyond the pounding rain. I scrambled crab-like behind an old freezer, the safest place in the room to protect myself from flying objects or errant bullets. I wasn't the only one taking shelter: six inches from my nose was a small hedgehog. Were hedgehogs dangerous? I made him a silent promise: I won't hurt you if you don't hurt me. At least he was unarmed.

When the shooting finally died down, I crawled back onto my cot. The next few hours passed fitfully and sleep evaded me.

The buttons of the man's uniform swelled beneath his girth. Sweat beaded on his forehead despite a desk fan pointing directly at him. A rock kept a pile of documents from flying away. An hour before, he'd reluctantly contacted the UN flight service on my behalf.

The MSF logistician had found me in the mud of the runway and half-carried me to the shack that served as "airport" office. Snot, sweat and mascara smeared my face.

"Wait! You can't leave her here!" the airport manager called after the disappearing logistician. Between great racking sobs, I blathered about the UN plane and pilot abandoning me. He handed me a glass of cloudy water and fidgeted with some papers.

"Sister, why do you cry? Do not fear. Things will work out. They always do."

Thirty thousand people displaced from Abeyi. Refugee camps in Darfur and warlords in Somalia. The LRA and their reign of terror in Uganda. Life is not a Hollywood movie. Things don't always "work out."

The logistician returned with the new nurse. Just a few hours ago, I'd handed the mission over to her, outlining our project goals, patient lists, supply inventory. I'd given her the laptop and keys and said good-bye with a quick hug and firm handshake. Her jaw dropped when she saw me now. I babbled about bloody soldiers, guns and Hollywood movie stars.

Like an obedient child, I swallowed the two yellow pills she handed me with a drink of the cloudy water. Frantic calls via satellite phone had been made to Khartoum and Nairobi, to MSF and UN headquarters. The ten milligrams of Valium stopped the palpitations, but not the sobbing. Worried frowns and quick glances were exchanged; I was known as a strong and confident leader.

"I can't do this anymore," I sobbed. "Do something. Get me out of here."

In the morning I searched for the hedgehog, but he was nowhere to be found. I shook my last clean MSF t-shirt to make sure he wasn't hiding inside. This last month of security threats had me on a razor edge. With only three or four hours sleep each night interrupted by gunfire and helicopters and nameless noises in the dark, my stomach twisted until I was unable to choke down one more hard-boiled egg. Ibuprofen refused to relieve my aching muscles or constant headaches. The computer screen blinded me after writing reports until too weary to fall asleep in my tiny room. At least a stinging gulp of vodka stopped the itching of countless bug bites.

Today I was to do an explo to document and assist the displaced. According to reports, over thirty thousand people were scattered throughout the countryside, exposed to the elements with little to protect them but scraggly Acacia trees. My driver and translator, Abdu, was a quiet man, tall and regal, indicative of the local Dinka people.

As we drove north, the sky before us grew ominous. Dark bilious clouds absorbed the horizon. They had the texture of the ocean, swirling and curling like waves. The day started without rain but the air was heavy as if at any moment, the heavens would open.

Abdu crept along slowly to keep our vehicle from getting stuck in the puddle-filled potholes. I began to grow irritated at our lack of progress when we passed a farmer herding five pathetically thin cows along the road. The black cotton soil had packed onto the bottom of the cows' hooves, and they balanced precariously on five-inch clumps.

"Look! The cows are wearing platform shoes!" I laughed. "Only in Sudan!"

Abdu rolled his eyes as I laughed at my joke. He continued at a snail's pace for about thirty minutes when my patience ran out.

"Stop driving like a little old lady," I snapped. "Speed up."

Abdu floored the pedal, and the Land Cruiser flew over the crest of a hill - right towards a lone soldier standing in the middle of the road, AK-47 pointed directly at our windshield.

"Stop!" I yelled. I could see the whites of the soldier's eyes, which meant he could also see mine. "Abdu! Stop before he shoots us!"

The Land Cruiser stopped ten feet from the soldier. Abdu and I slowly lifted our hands in plain view.

The soldier was little older than a boy and wore the

camouflage of the Southern People's Liberation Army. Weapon pointed, he cautiously moved toward us and studied the MSF logo on the side of our vehicle.

"Doctor?" he asked. "You are a doctor?"

We could discuss semantics later. When an armed man assumes you are a doctor, then you are a doctor.

He opened the door and yanked my arm, tearing the sleeve of my last clean t-shirt. Irritated, I managed to snatch the medical kit at my feet before he pulled me out. He dragged me past the corner of a rusted shed.

I'd expected to see clumps of brown grass and thorny shrubs. Instead there was utter chaos: a mass of bloody broken bodies, groaning and crying out beneath the sparse shade of Acacia trees. Dumfounded, I paused and forced down the rising taste of the morning's Nescafe.

Abdominal gunshot wounds. Some barely breathing. An arm with no hand. Legs and arms riddled with bullet holes. Bandages soaked red over stumps of arms. Gaping holes, where chins once were. Branches supported mangled legs. Blood bubbled from dark stained chests.

Back home, each one these men would have pre-hospital care and a critical care team waiting for their arrival. Here, there was just me. I couldn't save them all. The ER nurse in me took over. Triage was grotesquely simple: dying or not dying.

With no x-ray, I had to make quick judgements. If leg injuries could stand, they were stable. If not, they were unstable.

Strong pulse? Stable.

Weak pulse? Unstable.

No pulse? Close his eyes and move to the next.

I inched between moans and screams. Hands grabbed at me. The sweet smell of blood. I dug my fingers into bullet holes searching for exit wounds. Feeling the sharp prick of a bone fragment, I cursed. HIV rates were high. I would deal with the consequences later.

"Sister! Help my man. He is dying."

They pulled at my arms as I walked among the wounded.

"Come here now, Sister. He needs medicine."

"Sister! Sister! Sister!"

Pleas came from the soldier's "wives," women who followed their men from battle to battle. They stayed in makeshift camps, foraging and cooking, and washing dirty uniforms. The men provided for them; they cared for the men in return.

"Sister, you are doing good work," an officious voice boomed above me as I inserted an IV into a young man whose leg had been shattered. "Save my boys." With a quick upward glance, I could tell he was the authority here.

A young woman begged me to help her husband. She rocked his limp body in her arms. Knowing he couldn't survive the hour-long trip to the hospital, I gave him a shot of Morphine.

Suspicious soldiers pointed their guns at me demanding I attend their friends first. Not only did I not acquiesce, I got bossy. Move him there, get in, get out, do this, do that. To my surprise they followed my directions. The women soldiers were the best, especially after they watched me carry a man to a shady spot.

I put the wives to work. With gauze bandages placed over chests and abdomens, my instruction to "push hard" was met with fear. I grabbed one woman's hands and pressed down.

"Here like this." The women straightened their backs and crowded in to help. They held limbs and served as human IV poles. "If you hold the bag higher, it will be better for your man."

The first for transport were six men with chest wounds. Before boarding, I pointed to the window sticker showing a red circle/slash over an AK-47. MSF never allows weapons in their vehicles or in their hospitals. The men, too weak to protest, gave the weapons to their women who would follow on foot.

Abdu raised and secured the rear benches of the Land Cruiser and spread a blanket so four men could fit on the floor. Two more crowded into the front seat.

"Come with me, Sister?" Abdu trembled as he pondered shuttling the wounded back to the hospital. "Then if some die, my head won't end up on a chopping block."

"Go," I said, slamming the door. "And make sure you don't hit any of those cows in high heels."

By midday, two additional vehicles arrived to hurry the wounded to the surgical teams. Casualties continued showing up throughout the day. Despite my headache, I only drank small sips of warm water from my canteen. If I drank, I would have to pee and the there was no private spot. The wives offered bush meat cooked over an open fire, but I politely refused. I'd eaten rat once before, and it was not my protein of choice. I dug through my backpack searching for an energy bar, but all I found was a half-melted red Starburst from a care package. Sugary sweetness melted in my parched mouth.

I sighed in relief when a large, open-bed truck appeared as late afternoon shadows lengthened. The commander waved at me, to let me know this was his doing. The "walking wounded" were assisted aboard but resisted giving up their weapons which were often their only possession. My crossed arms made it clear: no guns allowed on the truck.

I wedged into the front of our MSF Land Cruiser between Abdu and an injured soldier. "Sorry," was Abdu's whispered shame, bruising my hip and thigh with the gear shift.

Three hours of sleep, and a soft knock snapped me awake. *Was it gunfire?* Reports said more injured soldiers had gathered beneath the Acacia trees. Abdu drove the Land Cruiser with more determination and confidence. As word spread, news crews from the United Nations, BBC and Al Jazeera had arrived before us. Nescafe rumbled in my empty stomach as I climbed down with my medical bag. Fortunately, today's injuries were less severe.

"The tourists have arrived," a cameraman from the UN approached me, tipping his head toward the microphones and tripods. "There must be big money in filming the horrors of war."

I ignored his comment and began triaging gunshot wounds to backs and legs and buttocks. The men were exhausted and submitted to care easily. I had finished dressing a wound when one of the media group, a good-looking man with a few days of beard, approached. The novelty of clean was hypnotic. He smelled really good and his white skin glowed. A skinny woman fussed over his every move.

"Hi, I'm Ben," he said as he offered his hand.

If you are going to meet a celebrity, you shower, comb your

hair and put on a bit of make-up. The best I'd managed today was to brush my teeth. My once-white MSF t-shirt was sour with sweat. Even a hedgehog wouldn't want to come near me.

"Hi, I'm Sue," I said to Ben Affleck. He was nice and seemed concerned about recent battles displacing people from Abyei. He hoped his celebrity status would shine attention on this barren part of the world where the government stood accused of brutalizing its own people.

"Hey, Sue can I ask something?" Ben's voice lowered.

"Fire away," I said. "No pun intended."

"If you had to use the bathroom, where would you go?"

I pointed him to an unoccupied spot behind a tree. The truth was, there was no privacy. I saw his assistant pass him a Kleenex. I wished him luck.

Did that really just happen? I thought to myself.

Day after day, the MSF machine hummed at full throttle. As Medical Coordinator, I was in charge. Geneva/Nairobi/Kampala/Juba flew us two planes a day of jerry cans for water, plastic sheeting for shelters, pea-nutty Plumpy Nut for malnourished children, medications and a full surgical set up. Local staff who fled Abyei found their way back to us. We set up distribution of Non Food Items at the school in Agok. Teams of medicals traveled the area offering mobile clinics. We erected tents to begin a nutrition program. With every large movement of people comes the risk of a deadly measles outbreak, so we planned mass vaccination campaigns.

Our little hospital swelled with more patients than beds. Yet even in their suffering, the tall, lean ebony-skinned Dinka women were stoic. Their children stared suspiciously at the soldiers, grabbing onto their mothers' colorful dresses if one came too close.

Despite poverty and war, babies must be born, and we delivered them. Cries of newborn joy over-shadowed the moans of war. Runny noses and bellies swelled from starvation. With Abyei destroyed, these people were stranded with no one to turn to but us.

The soldiers were getting cocky, bullying the civilian patients. To the locals, these were their "boys," heroes fighting for southern Sudan's independence. The commander grew aggressive, strutting with his AK-47 slung over his shoulder until I confronted him to put the gun outside the hospital gate. He kicked the "Guns Ma Taman (Guns Not Good)" signs and laughed as if it were a game. He barked at nurses and doctors alike, demanding care before the civilians. Now that the crisis was over, I was just a woman in his eyes, and he berated me. He demanded injections to cure "his boys." I gave them all tetanus shots.

Defeat after defeat, the southern army refused to stopped fighting. Lorries rumbled north to the front line. The soldiers in our hospital malingered, invoking new symptoms and refusing discharge. The commander never left. He prowled too close when I talked to patients, upsetting them and making me nervous. The stink of his body odor was masked by fresh doses of perfume. He brushed my shoulder when I sat to review patients' charts. I slammed the charts closed, and he walked away, laughing that great belly laugh which I'd grown to despise.

Sleep wouldn't come. Puffy bruises hung under my sandpaper eyes. I was haunted by images of bloody chests, severed limbs and women wailing over dead men. Overcome with guilt that I'd be going home soon, I pushed myself harder.

Any whiff of food nauseated me, and I couldn't tolerate one more mouthful of mushy pasta and boiled eggplant swimming in oil. The local ash-covered bread scraped my teeth like fingernails on a blackboard.

A box arrived from Juba with oranges and peanut butter. My stomach had become used to being empty and rejected food. Vomiting Nescafe is worse than drinking it in the first place. I took a piece of IV tubing and strung it through the loops of my jeans. Each day I had to tie it a little tighter to keep them from falling off.

One humid afternoon while changing the bandages of an amputee, I startled as a soldier banged the metal bedframe, waking a woman who had just had a C-section. He demanded she give up her bed. Eyes downcast, she picked up her newborn and slid to a mat on the floor.

One of our female doctors confronted the bully, demanding he leave. They stood eye to eye, unblinking, chests rising and falling with rage.

"Woman, I will hit you if you don't move," he growled, gripping the neck of a Coke bottle. The commander appeared. He raised an eyebrow and gestured at the doctor's chest with thumb and index finger in classic pistol form. I intervened.

"We have taken care of all your injured," I said, my eyes fixed firmly on his. "But this is a hospital. This is a doctor. You cannot continue to threaten us and the other patients." Weeks before, this man begged me to provide medical care to his troops. We had worked together, side by side. He'd even thanked me.

He put his hand down after clicking the "pistol" at me and stalked out of the ward. The new mother stayed on her mat. The doctor and I silently turned, clasping shaking hands.

Bugs. Annoying, irritating bugs. Day after day. Bugs that drive you crazy. No wonder cows swat them with their tails. The nights were infested with bugs. Long-winged flying bugs, buzzing mosquitos, biting whoknowswhat bugs. Big bugs, little bugs. Bugs that snuck through the mesh of my net. Ugly bugs. Bugs I had never seen before. They swarmed my headlamp and smacked the glowing screen of my laptop. Darkness fell at six pm, and I squirreled away in my office/bedroom/storage room working on never-ending reports. Bugs crunched beneath my feet. It was a curse of Biblical proportions. I pulled the mosquito net over my bed and scraped out as many as possible. I slapped at them when they landed on my neck.

The dust destroyed my last pair of contact lenses. I reverted back to an old pair of bifocals, but after accidently sitting on them, they were bent and misshapen and sat askew on my nose. I knew I looked foolish but I didn't care. I had a job to do.

Many of the expat and national staff showed symptoms of anxiety and stress. They would seek me out while I tried to complete reports and order supplies. The ticking of the clock on my cardboard-box-now-bedside-table allowed me to only half listen to their fears. I hated that their tears frustrated me. As a leader, I knew I should be empathetic but there was so much to do. Crying just gets in the way.

There was a soft knock and team members' voices outside my door. I had nothing left to offer them tonight. My compassion was all used up. My strength had leaked out. I felt only sharp gray edges. Like a coward, I clicked off my headlight, rolled up my spare pair of jeans as a pillow and lay still in the darkness.

My departure date arrived several days too late.

Four hours I sat like stone. Empty. Achy. Voices and people moved outside me. The next flight could take me to Wau and then to Juba. The log led me to the steps of the plane and wished me a safe journey. What did it matter?

Wau was more of the same. Dirt. Bugs. Brush. Cows. And no onward flight to Juba. Again I sat.

I broke all security rules by buying a seat on an "off limits" commercial plane. The pilot was kind and I had cash. I knew such flights could be dangerous but what could be worse than what I'd just faced for the past month? I didn't care what kind of trouble I'd get into. I refused to stay stranded one more day.

The sky was cloudy. "Rain's coming," I thought as we lifted off. I thought I would feel relief; instead my mind was black. Colorless. Beyond void. I have no memory of the flight, just the bumping hops when we landed in Juba. Through the window I saw an array of United Nations planes sitting on the tarmac.

The mud on my backpack had dried and flaked off in chunks as I walked out of the terminal and called for a driver.

A baboon strolled around the parking lot swinging his head side to side as if to wonder, "Where did I leave my car?" Instead of a laugh, a sob came. What had started as a dream had left me feeling a total failure: joining MSF, travelling to faraway places to help the most desperate and poor of our world, giving of my skills and knowledge. And heart.

I left Sudan. Empty. Guilty. Broken.

I wonder if Ben Affleck ever felt that way.

Redemption

I finished my 2008 southern Sudan mission a demoralized, exhausted mess. Counseling and crying erased the numbness, and my pain blurred over time. But it wasn't until a year later, meeting one of the nurses from the Abyei mission for lunch in Vancouver, when I was finally able to gain perspective on my failure.

"It got worse after you left," Nancy stared out the window as her hands shredded her napkin. "I could only sleep a few hours at night. Even the scratch of a mouse would startle me. I stopped eating. Connor had to remind me to take a bite of this or that. And I chain smoked those godawful cigarettes they sold there."

I was taken aback. This was supposed to be *my* confession, *my* apology. But my words were coming from her mouth. Her sorrow and embarrassment mirrored mine.

I listened as she poured her heart out, picking distractedly at chipped nail polish. She apologized for her tears, but sorrowful memories leaked from their hiding place. I understood. We all do what we must to survive.

Things got better, she said, since she and Connor moved to

rural Canada. They'd met on that mission, and shared the horrors of war, guilt, anger and sadness. He too saw the best and worst humanity has to offer.

I confessed my lingering feelings of guilt for failing to support the team enough, for isolating and hiding. *I could have done more. I should have taken on more of your burdens.*

But our words crossed paths. Our need to speak overcame our capacity to listen.

"I did everything I could in those final weeks," she continued. "We worked around the clock but with no support staff, it was just us with the moms and the babies, twenty-four-seven. They were so sick. No matter how hard or long we worked, they just kept dying. Not nearly enough of them lived."

Now I listened, trying to make up for the one thing I didn't have the time or energy for in Agok. I'd been too caught up in the war between life and death. Wrapped in our own protective bubbles, focused on caring for patients, we had isolated ourselves from the horrors and each other.

"One patient was a small malnourished girl with Down's syndrome," Nancy's voice became soft. "Ajok was the sweetest, cuddliest little thing, but I didn't feel she was well enough to leave even though her mother wanted her to be discharged. Mama was a champion, fighting hard against a world that devalues any disability. I used my status, Expat Nurse Who Knows What's Best, and convinced the mom they should stay. When the fighting started, the hospital was one of the first targets. Eyewitnesses told me bodies were piled high - patients, family members, staff. But I wasn't in that pile because my white skin was my ticket out."

We sat in silence while the server refilled our coffee mugs.

"I went back to find them, but they weren't there. To this day I hope beyond hope that the mother and her beautiful child survived. But I know in my heart they were in that pile, and my ignorance and arrogance put them there."

We looked at each other. No more words came. We knew. We understood. We accepted. We forgave. And we hugged goodbye.

It's 2016 and once again I enter the hornet's nest as Medical Coordinator for Doctors Without Borders, but this time with eyes wide open. Juba has changed. There are paved roads with traffic lights and traffic jams, ten story buildings and construction. Restaurants have air conditioning and CNN playing on flat screen TVs. And yet it hasn't improved. The street in front of our office/house still has the same rain-carved ruts I remember. There is still no city power; only generators polluting with noise and soot.

This brand new sparkling country, eager and full of hope five years ago, is again broken. The 2011 referendum for independence from Sudan was essentially unanimous. International aid poured in to set up the world's newest democracy, rich with oil reserves, ripe for exploitation.

But power sharing did not come naturally to the two revolutionary leaders, and the country split apart along tribal lines. Oil was "pre-sold" and the proceeds spent or stolen. International partners went home. The currency deflates daily. Juba is again filled with white Toyota Land Cruisers, symbol of Non-Governmental Organizations around the world. NGOs provide services the South

Sudan government is unable to sustain. People have lost hope, and every day is a new battle for survival.

The 2016 Independence Day celebration was cancelled due to lack of funds.

Things are completely different and still the same. Our old office building still stands, but the corner lot where I had my tent full of emergency medical supplies is now a hotel with rooftop bar. The Queen of Sheba bar, our favorite after work "office," burned down, but the popular places on the Nile now have concrete floors instead of dirt. Baboons still stroll, tails held high. Children still splash and catch fish with mosquito nets along the riverbank while their mothers wash clothes nearby. The dogs are the same – thin, long legged, mangy yellow creatures.

The exhausted outgoing MedCo briefs me, and I gulp at how much there is to do. Measles is rampant and meningitis may hit hard this year. Malaria cases should drop since the rains have stopped, but we need to prepare for cholera when the Rainy Season begins again in a few months. Besides epidemics, tropical diseases and snake bites, there are inexperienced field staff, not enough resources to meet the demands of the population, ongoing cattle raids, fighting and uneasy tension.

Best of all, I get to revisit Agok. I've divorced most negative memories and approach with the unease of anticipation. What started with mobile clinics from the back of my Land Cruiser is now a full-fledged 160 bed hospital. There are still tents, hastily thrown up to handle surges in measles cases (which need to be isolated from the general population). But there is a real ER, Maternity and Newborn care, an Operating Theater and recovery room, Lab and Pharmacy, inpatient care for men, women and children.

Unfortunately, there is still the need for a malnutrition program where tiny frail little ones battle to consume calories. There is a sprawling living compound for the nearly 100 national and international staff working here. A yellow two-part transport vehicle stands ready on snowplow treads to brave patient transfers through the Rainy Season mud between here and satellite project Mayom.

I'm amazed on my tour and can't stop saying "Wow!"

After the evening meal, an all-staff meeting is called. I introduce myself. "I came eight years ago, when Abyei and its hospital were destroyed and the people ran here to Agok. We started with few staff and supplies, but did our best."

To my amazement, the entire team stood in applause.

"This was the nurse who saved our people." Abdu spoke loudly. He was no longer a driver, but instead held the esteemed position as a Human Resources Assistant. "She is a strong woman. We thank you on behalf of the people of Agok who now have this wonderful hospital to help them stay healthy."

I'm embarrassed, but allow Abdu these moments of boasting. He, too, needs to grasp at the threads of success in a world where injustices abound. Like so many other places in the world, the Have's are getting stronger while the Have Not's struggle to make sense of it.

Just a few months after my return home, civil war has returned to South Sudan. The economy is in ruins. The currency is worthless. People flee Juba for the countryside in hopes of avoiding violence. Hospitals are torched and international aid workers have been tortured and raped. The NGOs are leaving.

All our hard work, destroyed, then rebuilt, only to be destroyed again. At times I wonder. And wonder some more.

The Jim Campbell Story:
A Tale of Lies, Deceit and Betrayal

"*Call me, I'm back in Seattle*," was Sue's abrupt email.

Her Northend Hospital ER colleagues looked at one other in open-mouthed disbelief. According to their calculations, Sue just passed the two-thirds mark on her six-month Doctors Without Borders (MSF) mission in Habila, a small village she called the "Nostril of Darfur" poking west into Chad.

Before the catastrophic war, conflicts between tribes in Darfur were traditionally settled in age-old variations on "an eye for an eye." Arab nomads hauled goods to trade in the marketplace on Tuesdays and Thursdays, drank glasses of sweet tea under shade trees and returned by camel to their skin-covered encampments each night. The river slowed in a right angle curve, allowing precious water to be shared by all - animals and irrigation and drinking and washing. Small garden patches and mango trees lined the riverbanks. Shallow hand-dug wells provided water when the rains stopped, and the riverbed dried to a swath of sand. Crops and fish were dried and stored for the upcoming hunger gap before the next harvest. Donkeys complained of their heavy workloads while dogs boasted and gossiped through the night. Women collected firewood and pounded sorghum and okra for dinner. Children fashioned toys from clay and bits of wire. Outsiders were rarely seen. No electric lights marred the brightness of the night stars. Prayers were private.

And then it changed. 6000 inhabitants became 31,000, and Habila became a refuge. The International Criminal Court indicted Sudan's president and vice president on charges of genocide and funding the Arab nomads renamed "Janjaweed." Their mandate was to destroy the rebellious black African tribes in the western half of Sudan known as Darfur. Widespread terror and destruction followed. Villages were razed by helicopter gunships and the residents were killed, kidnapped and raped. International reports surfaced of the systematic obliteration of villages and the murder of hundreds of thousands of residents. Nearly two million people were driven from their homes to find sanctuary in more secure areas within Darfur and Chad.

"Scorched earth policy" was literal rather than figurative with massacres and entire villages burned to the ground. Google Earth satellites offered proof of the devastation, and celebrities rallied to bring attention in the aftermath of the carnage.

But by the time the world took notice, it was too late.

Sue's team of three expats had taken over management of a one-room brick "hospital" and provided medical care in MSF's free, non-partisan, independent style for the isolated and harassed people of West Darfur. In the absence of local doctors or nurses, she hired and trained a quasi-medical staff to provide basic services like treatment for malaria and malnutrition and trauma.

Isolation and lack of social outlets had taken their toll on the small team. Sue's emails were increasingly filled with heartbreaks and work challenges as well as hard-won achievements. Her friends at home worried at her change in tone.

And now, suddenly, she was back home in Seattle. All feared that something bad must have happened. They repeatedly dialed Sue's home number but got only her voice mail.

TeriAnn volunteered, "If you cover my patients, I'll drive over to her house right now and find out what's going on."

It was Kelley, a former over-attentive-to-detail ICU nurse, who rolled her eyes with a groan. "Look at the date of the email, guys," she said.

April 1st, 2005.

Even from her isolation in Sudan, with a simple one line e-mail, Sue had pulled an April Fools' prank on her friends and had drawn a virtual line in the hot, Sudanese sand.

Over the course of four years of working together, nurses Sue, Kelley, TeriAnn and Bette had become the heart and soul of Northend ER and were affectionately nicknamed "The Four Horsewomen of the Apocalypse." They inter-mingled humor and play with hard work and high expectations for patient care. Those were the days before Press Ganey began to measure patient satisfaction scores and pain became "the fifth vital sign," when ER nursing was actually fun.

TeriAnn showed her coworkers an email she'd received from Sue five days earlier:

"Our bleak life trudges on. Work is interesting – how do you measure a fever when the ambient temperature is 130 degrees? EVERYONE feels hot! At least I figured out how to have Happy Hour in a no-alcohol country: ice cream. Yep, I figured out: I mix powdered milk, powdered creamer, sugar and some mango or Nescafe for flavor, put it in an enamel-covered steel pot in our vaccine freezer, and stir it every couple hours. By evening, it's ice cream! Our cleaner tried it and the next day came to work with a scarf wrapped around her neck (remember, it's 130 degrees) because she had never had anything cold before. There's no electricity or appliances or running water in the village, so I'm sure ice cream is other-worldly.

"Our world is small. We work 6 ½ days a week, which is probably good because there's nothing much to do otherwise. The DVD drive on my laptop burned out in the heat, and I've read Gone With The Wind twice. We have to put our work computers on ice packs to keep them running. The air is Rye Krisp dry. I'm constantly drinking water but rarely peeing which is actually a mixed blessing since there are only squat latrines, not toilets. I have thighs of steel but might go into kidney failure. HA HA!

"We only get MSF intra-net, not 'real' internet access, so we can't even play online for distraction. Did I tell you – to download emails, one of us has to hold the big Turaya satellite phone and point the antennae while another of us calls out when the signal gets strong enough. Then everyone freezes in that position for about 4 or 5 minutes until all messages have downloaded.

"What's going on in Seattle these days? I'm dying here, starving for news, weather, gossip, lies, anything!"

That was the opening! Sue had essentially begged for retaliation. The plot was hatched.

"The story has to have a man in it," TeriAnn said with her New York twang. "And of course, if there's a man, there's Bette. This is revenge, ladies, R-E-V-E-N-G-E!"

Bette's creative mind ran rampant. A sexual liaison would be the juiciest hook, and having found herself single yet again, she could play the femme fatale to a tee. Being a Canadian traveling nurse, she could create fresh stories at the drop of an eyelash.

They huddled around a work computer as TeriAnn typed.

"There's a new doctor here, a friend of Dr. Pudge. Apparently they did their ER residencies together in Chicago. He's cute and nice and takes good care of his patients."

The next day Sue responded.

"Man, I gotta get home soon!"

With giggles, the web spinning had begun.

"Too late. Bette said she had to get to him before you did, so they already went out. HA HA! She said they hit it off great. But keep this between us. She doesn't want everyone to know since it's a work thing..."

The spiders excitedly awaited Sue's response. It was as predicted.

"Damn that Bette! Here I am in Darfur, saving the world, and she gets the only cute straight guy who ever worked at Northend ER!

"Things are moving so incredibly slowly here. I decided to teach our 'medicals' how to do blood transfusions. We've lost so many patients to severe malaria and hemorrhage in childbirth, I felt it imperative we start even though there is no lab much less a blood bank. We use a Hemocue for hematocrits – you put a drop of blood in a ViewFinder (like we had as kids), hold it up to the light and visually match the hue of red against a standard. Teaching them how to do blood typing was wild.

"Remember in high school when you put four drops of blood on a white tile, then added the drops and it agglutinated to indicate Type A, B, AB and O? Well, no one even wanted me to draw their blood until they saw the clumping happen – it was like magic! HA HA! Then they all crowded in, 'Me next! Me next!'

"But the biggest challenge is finding someone to donate – even family members are reluctant. These patients wouldn't die if they were simply born in the developed world. But that's a lament for another day.

"Keep me up to date with this Bette thing and remember, I WANT DETAILS! By the way, does this guy have a name?"

Blank faces. What could the made-up mystery man be called? Something easy. Something generic. Something that couldn't be screwed up.

"Jim Campbell," TeriAnn sent.

"Okay, we've got her," gloated Bette after bringing a new patient from Triage. "Now we need to weave the threads. Sue knows I'm getting it on with this hot new guy, and she knows I want to keep it secret. Next?"

Kelley stepped up to the plate. Being a true-blue, corn-fed, Midwest wife and mother, Sue would never suspect her of duplicity. Kelley was known as a straight shooter with strong moral boundaries. She played her character perfectly.

"Did you hear we hired a new doctor named Jim Campbell? He's mid 30's, brown hair, nice looking and pleasant enough to work with – unlike his buddy Dr. Pudge - ugh!

"But yesterday I had weird encounter with him. Tell me what you think: the medics brought an 83 yr old female with a CHF

exacerbation. They couldn't get an IV but gave nitro en route, pressure 60/40 and lethargic. It was one of those 'oh crap!' moments. I cut off her clothes and got the line. Her sats were low, so Dr. Campbell decided to intubate her, ordered Lasix and dopamine.

"The whole time, he stood really close even though there's plenty of space in Room 2 to move around without running into each other. He even squeezed my shoulder while I was listening to the patient's lungs. I was a little taken aback, but continued to take care of the patient. He complimented me on how calm I stayed and how we were 'really in synch.' I turned red, stammered a polite 'thank you' and left the room. I was so embarrassed and uncomfortable! I avoided him the rest of the shift, but no one else seemed to have a problem with him.

"I told my hubby after putting the baby to bed, and was he pissed off! He demands I tell our simpering manager plus Dr. Pudge. But Pudge is the doc-in-charge AND Campbell's best friend! I mean, it's going to get me in trouble, right? Even Bette likes him, and you know how tough she is with doctors.

"What do you think? What would you do?"

Kelley reported back to her co-conspirators. "Ladies, the bait's been set. All we have to do now is wait."

But not for long.

Sue must have been downloading at that same moment. *"Right this minute, you go to talk with the manager, simpering though she may be, and Pudge. And I mean NOW! Period. Sexual harassment is in the eye of the beholder. Tell what happened and how it made you feel. There doesn't need to be 'punishment,' but it is YOUR responsibility to say NO and tell the bosses. If they don't take you seriously, go up the chain of command. Do not allow another day to go by nor let anybody talk you out of taking this to the next level. Innocent or not, he needs to realize what he is doing and how it is affecting others.*

"GOT IT???????

"And I want to hear back from you in two days.

"Hugs and strength from one who has plenty to spare. Sue."

The next morning at work, Kelley shared Sue's email. The spiders raised their Starbucks cups in a toast to their cleverness. But Sue was no fool. Their responses and timing had to be impeccable.

Together, they crafted Kelley's reply, explaining that in hindsight, she may have overreacted. Jim had apologized for upsetting her and had "personal space issues" he was working out. He said he respected her, knew her to be devoted to her family, and valued their working relationship.

"He seemed really sincere. Thanks for caring all the way from Darfur – I think I'll sit down and have a bowl of Tillamook ice cream and think of you. Can't wait for you to join me. Don't worry about Jim! We're fine."

Kelley let out a diabolical laugh as she clicked "send."

News of the ruse spread throughout the ER, and others wanted to join in the fun. They were warned: Act only as directed, acknowledge the presence of the new doctor and otherwise play dumb.

Another RN, code name "The Kitten" agreed to be the next target. TeriAnn sent Sue a gossipy email about The Kitten grumbling that Dr. Campbell rubbed against her while she was taking care of a patient.

Sue sent an email to Kelley. *"Just got an email from TeriAnn saying another RN complained that Dr. Campbell approached her in a similar fashion to you. That may influence your thoughts on going to a higher level with your concerns. Maybe talk to TeriAnn if she hasn't already told you?"*

Kelley replied *"This is news to me. I need to figure out what's going on. Thanks for the heads up – from halfway around the world!"*

But Sue was nobody's fool. She reached out to Lorena, one of the ER Unit Clerks, who could always be counted on for inside information. But the spiders were one page ahead in the script.

"Hey Lorena, I'm hearing things about this new Dr. Campbell. What's going on? Do you know anything? Let me know whatever you find out – you're always a good sleuth!! Love, Sue"

Lorena, Sue's ever loyal confidante, played dumb. *"Hi, I can't find out nothing. TeriAnn and them seem to be talking about him but when I go near, they clam up. If I find something out, I'll write you right away. He seems like a nice man, but I haven't really worked with him. Love, Lorena."*

Next, Sue contacted her long-time friend, Dr. Mike. But Bette had already dealt him a hand, and Dr. Mike played it well.

"Hey Sue, I haven't heard much of anything, but you know with me working only night shift, I'm the last to know. I'll keep my ears open, but there's no doc's meeting for a while. I'll let you know if I hear anything. You know I am always on the nurse's side. Lots of love, Mike"

Lots of love, indeed.

Sue, isolated and lonely in Sudan, devoured the emails and

shared her incredulity with her expat workmates at their daily Happy Hour. The Ethiopian doctor asked, "Are you sure they're not playing with you?"

"I don't think so …"

Time was running out. TeriAnn fleshed out the devious next steps. "Ladies, we need to hurry up and blow Sue away before her end of mission. Act 2: Bette goes to Hawaii and Jim surprises her, sweeps her off her feet and they get married on the beach! Back in the ER, Kelley goes to our manager and Dr. Pudge, but nothing can be done because Jim is on vacation (in Hawaii chasing Bette!). Far-fetched but worth a try. Let's hit her hard and fast."

It was Bette's turn to write: "*What great work you are doing in Sudan! When you get back I'd love to talk about your motivation for volunteering. Hey, don't know if you heard about the new doc. Can you keep a secret? He's sweet on me. After all the losers I've dated over the years, I feel like I've won the lottery. I wish I could change my holiday and not go to Hawaii after all – I'll miss him!*"

At the same time, TeriAnn emailed Sue: *"That jerk Campbell made a pass at me! It was just after we resuscitated a 30 year old heroin overdose. He put his hand on my arm and said I was the best he'd ever had. I was spitting mad – apparently, he doesn't know Bette and I are good friends. Tomorrow I'm going to management to complain. I tried calling Bette but her phone went to voice mail, and I didn't want to leave a message. She's off to Hawaii for a week – probably best that she's going to be out of town when this goes down. Stay safe."*

A third email flew, this time from Kelley to Sue: *"TeriAnn and I finally had a shift together and talked about Dr. Campbell dating Bette. I opened up about how he made me feel, and TeriAnn was pissed because apparently he hit on her as well. We marched to the back office, but our lame manager was quiet as a clam, nodding her head and smiling. Dr. Pudge's face went white, and he let out a sigh as if he'd heard it before. He said he's known Jim since med school and suggested we were overreacting. He said he would 'look into' things, but Jim had taken a couple weeks off so he'd get back to us later."*

Sue immediately emailed TeriAnn: *"I knew Kelley wasn't the only one he would do that to, and encouraged her to tell management. Sexual harassment in the workplace is a federal crime, and he needs to be fired.*

"I'm sad for Bette. She is a bright woman, but I am afraid she will blame this all on you and not him."

The next email from Sue was to Dr. Mike. *"What the hell is going on in that ER? First I hear about Bette and Dr. Jim getting it on, now I hear he's harassing pretty much the entire female staff! Apparently, they complained to management but nothing happened. It's hard being so far away and hearing such terrible things happening at home. I'm afraid this is going to really disrupt the great environment we have there. Please do what you can, ok?"*

Mike was beginning to waver. Sue told him she'd developed a fever and symptoms of malaria, and he didn't want to place more stress on her. The Three Spiders pressured him to be true to his word. In the end he agreed to write one more email, but he would be vague.

"I tried to find out from Pudge, but everyone seems to be playing their cards close to their chests. The nurses are buzzing, but no one

will come out and say what's going on. I have my ears open and I am ready to help where I can."

There was no doubt Sue was feeling the heat beneath the unrelenting Darfur sun. During the day she pushed her team as well as herself to continue their lifesaving work. But the evening download of soap opera emails was enticing nectar no one could resist. Her companions were as eager to hear the next installment as she was.

From Sue to TeriAnn: *"As her friend, you should talk to Bette after they fire his sorry ass. Be there to support her and answer her questions, but don't tell her anything she doesn't have to know. It will only hurt her. Talk to her as a nurse and encourage her to get a gyne exam for STDs. I don't trust that guy in the least.*

"Funny how it is clearer for me to see from halfway around the world than you guys right there faced with it. The thing is, people like that don't change. They victimize and victimize until they are forced to stop.

"On another note, I'm dead on my feet and faint and nauseated and crappy. I'm headed back to bed. Heather sent me the new Rob Thomas CD but with this high fever, I thought he was in the tent with me. At least not being able to hold anything down means I don't have to pee 'cuz I don't think I could walk across the sand to squat right now."

For a moment, Bette felt bad. Thinking of Sue, isolated and sick … thirsty for connection with the outside world. Yet it was impossible to unravel the web that had been so intricately woven. Besides, pulling her pigtail was so much fun.

Bette began to compose: *"Sorry to bother you in Africa, but it seems people I thought were my friends have involved you in my personal business. I know it's not your fault. Some people apparently can't keep their noses out of places they don't belong. I don't know why they started all these vicious rumors about Jim. He is an amazing man and a true humanitarian. They are jealous and obviously have some motivation to keep me from being happy for the first time in forever. Maybe they're jealous and miserable in their own lives. Whatever! Ignore everything they said. If all that nonsense were true, would he had travelled to Hawaii to marry me? It's true! Can you believe it!*

"With all this backstabbing and nastiness, we are going to have to leave Northend ER and find a new home. Jim says California is nice, and he has friends there. Can I use you for a reference for a new job once we get there?

"Again, sorry to bother you when you're doing so much to make the world a better place."

Bette called for the final act in their payback play. "We have her eating out of our hands. I think it's time to have a good laugh and drop her on her head. The piece de resistance? Since Geoff is openly gay, have him email her about The Villain making a pass at him. Make it flamboyant and hysterical so she knows she's been had. Game over!"

Sue immediately replied to Geoff's tittering tease of an email: *"Geoffy, my love, do not do this. For many reasons. I have heard about him from several people and am more than a bit concerned about the stories they've told. You have a wonderful partner in Bob, and it would be incredibly sad for you to throw that all away on this creep.*

"I should be home at the end of the month - Party at my house!

See you soon and listen to Sister Sue: Keep your zipper zipped and stick with a good thing."

Then supportive words for Bette: *"Quite wonderful to hear from you after all that has happened. Can't believe you got married on the beach in Hawaii. That's crazy! As far as the gossip, it's hard to makes sense of it all from so far away. When I get home, let's go for a drink and talk. It's too hard to say some things via email. And don't worry, if you feel the need to get a new job, I have lots of contacts."*

The web was woven tighter than predicted; it would take a bit longer to break through.

A simple email arrived from Mike: *"You know that guy we were talking about? When he comes back from Hawaii he's going to get the can. That's all I know right now."*

Sue to TeriAnn: *"Oh my God!!!!! A little bird told me Jim is going to get what is coming to him – as in 'Bye, bye, birdie.' I really thought this was going to be a belated April Fools joke, but now I think it's real. You guys are not clever, devious or coordinated enough to mess with me this badly!*

"Everyone, and I mean EVERYONE in Habila knows the story. We are holding our breath waiting for each and every email to hear what's happening. I even started downloading three times a day instead of two!

"Last night Bette wrote to me for the first time. She is very upset, in love and believes he is in love with her, too. As I said before, she will believe him over you. It is a no win for anyone. Be there to pick her up after she falls apart. She will be a frickin' wreck. She's the one I feel sorriest for. How do you retain your dignity after that?

"Write me ten times a day with updates. My poor dear little ER is falling apart, and I can't do anything to help."

The tone of her emails told them she still hadn't figured out the joke. Time to drop the hammer so she'd have had time to calm down before heading home.

True Blue Kelley wrote next: *"I found out Jim went to Hawaii and married Bette – apparently they had a thing going on for weeks even though he was hitting on every employee in the ER. Can you believe it? I thought Bette had more sense than that! Anyway, I was so mad, I got his phone number from the nurse's station and really laid into him. As Bette's friend, I felt it my duty to defend her.*

"Then you know what happens? He starts crying! He tells me that everything is so messed up, he doesn't know how to fix things. He says he is meeting TeriAnn for drinks and could I please join them to talk this out? I said fine. Whatever. It doesn't change things.

"I get there after work and guess what? No TeriAnn! Then he spilled the beans about Bette. He cares about her and doesn't want to hurt her, but he never wanted to be married to her. She's too "out there" for him. She was the one who planned the whole wedding on the beach thing, and he didn't know how to back out and now his life is a mess.

"He said he was in love from the moment he first saw me! He knows I'm married and have a son, so he distracted himself with Bette but then she got so wacko. He said it's obvious I'm not happy, and he sees passion in my eyes. He kissed me, and I felt truly alive again. Not a mother. Not a wife. A woman again!

"So brace yourself.

"I'm leaving with Jim to California in the morning. I know you may not agree with my decision, but I know deep down this is the right thing to do. I'm sorry I won't be here when you get back and hope we can keep in touch. Thank you for all the inspiration you've

given me. If I could be half the nurse you are, I could only be so lucky."

"They're messing with you," the Ethiopian doctor shook his head after Sue read Kelley's latest email aloud at Happy Hour. "Show us the pictures again about who is who?"

She had told her mission companions of her send-off-to-Darfur party at Dr. Mike's house, aptly dubbed "Kiss My Ass Good-Bye." Two chocolate mounds formed the cake. Bette wore a fake plastic bum all night, offering it for lipstick covered kisses. Geoff danced in a flowing white gown chanting "Kiss! Kiss! Kiss!" as the beer bottles emptied. Gifts and keepsakes piled up but couldn't be included in Sue 22 kilo luggage restriction. Photos caught the mood of the evening.

She pulled out her favorite - a picture of Bette, TeriAnn and Kelley, sitting side by side on the couch, drinks in hand, mocking the proverbial "Hear no evil, See no evil, Speak no evil."

At that moment she realized. She'd been duped.

"I finally figured you all out, but now everyone here is disappointed the soap opera is over. My hat is off to you. But in a sad, sick way, I wish it was true and I'd have more installments to look forward to. HA HA!

"Is any of it true? Is there a Jim Campbell?"

When Sue returned to Northend Emergency Room, she met handsome Dr. Richards, who coincidently was a med school classmate with Dr. Pudge in Chicago and had started to work in the ER while she was in Darfur. Much to his bewilderment, she burst out laughing when they were introduced and called him "Jim."

Yei

The first time I heard the Celine Dion song, I sang along.

The same song played an hour later, and I hummed as I rolled over, trying to find a comfortable position on the yoga mat masquerading as a hotel mattress. I had already padded the wooden slats underneath with every spare t-shirt and ratty hotel towel I could find, but they still poked into my back and hips.

It had been an exhausting day. After several hours of travel from Juba HQ with our Emergency Response to Epidemics Team, I'd met with the UN coordinator and the doctor in charge of the local hospital in Yei, which was overwhelmed by a Cholera outbreak. By nine o'clock in the evening, I was ready for sleep, however the Canadian songstress had other plans for me as she serenaded the bar outside my hotel window.

I'm your lady and you are my man...

An infinite video loop played on the TV perched on a shelf just out of my reach. As her voice warbled over and over, the high notes pierced through my eyeballs and down my spine. I suppressed the urge to throw the contents of my room at the screen. I was no longer humming.

I peered through my window into the bar. Several groups of men argued animatedly from wobbly plastic chairs around stained tables, smoking and drinking hard liquor. Some wore military uniforms. Their voices rose in competition with Celine and a second TV playing an old American western movie.

In Africa, it seemed, there was no room for dead air space.

I took a sleeping pill but couldn't turn off my mind or body. Even with my special trick of adding lotion to my earplugs, the cacophony was impossible to ignore.

The hotel was reasonable by southern Sudan standards. The financial manager of our team demanded frugality with funds and booked the cheapest rooms. Fifteen dollars per night got you a bed with a thin vinyl mattress and a lamp on a rickety bedside table. My lamp wouldn't turn on; it had no light bulb.

The communal toilet and shower were located on the far side of the bar. Twenty-five dollars would have bought each of us a room with its own bathroom. "Extravagant" perhaps, but it would have been a welcome luxury.

I'm usually careful to restrict fluid intake in uncertain places, but the heat and humidity had begged me to drink several bottles of water at meetings earlier in the afternoon. Try as I might, I could no longer ignore Celine or my bladder.

The clusters of men grew quiet as I navigated legs and chairs, toilet paper wadded into my fist. Disgusted by the filth of the only bowl, I chose to squat over the hole in the floor. The men watched me return to my room. I heard laughter as I closed and locked my door.

The electronics blessedly fell silent at midnight, and the men stumbled away. I nestled onto my lumpy slats and vowed to talk to the manager about the noise.

In the morning the hotel manager, a tall wiry man with a shaved head and a large gap between his front teeth, shrugged at my complaints. He smugly raised an eyebrow to the bartender, whose bloodshot eyes gave evidence of the previous night's activities. I recognized that look. Proud. Defiant. Uncompromising. I decided to keep the rest of my concerns to myself.

Frayed towel and soap in hand, I walked across the dirt floor in my flip flops, through the now empty bar to the toilets and shower. There was only one actual toilet, missing a seat and too disgusting to use. The rest were squat latrines. My thighs groaned as I did my business quickly.

Beside the latrine was a big barrel of water heating over a wood fire. I dipped out a bucketful and carried it to a curtained-off area, frugally using the warm water for what's known as a "bucket shower." The technique is to stand in a large plastic tub, pour water over one's body, soap up, shampoo the hair, then douse oneself with cups full of water until rinsed off. The gray water in the tub is then used to wash your clothes.

The hotel's breakfast was a cold, greasy fried egg, dry piece of bread and a fly-speckled jar of strawberry jam. Pushing them aside, I opened a packet of instant coffee I'd brought from home, hoping to be revived. There was no kettle or mug in our rooms so I absconded with hot water from behind the bar when backs were turned.

I met up with the Austrian logistics coordinator (the man

responsible for booking our rooms) in the "dining room": a raised concrete pad off to one side of the bar. The dark circles under his eyes told me his night had passed as painfully as my own. Celine called again as we left the motel together.

Near, far, wherever you are ...

In 2008 Yei was a bustling town and the headquarters of the rebel Southern People's Liberation Army, which had been battling for independence from the government in the North for twenty years. People lived close to the ground. There were no paved roads or sidewalks. A myriad of bikes and motorcycles cluttered the roadways, but most people got around by "footing." Crossing the road reminded me of an old video game where a frog tries to hop across a busy street without being squashed.

The rainy season gouged deep ruts and potholes into the hard packed clay, assuring constant work for vehicle repair shops. For the moment the rain had stopped, but Cholera bacteria had already been flushed into the town's water supply. Clouds again threatened the hot, humid sky.

The sights and sounds were unlike anything in America. I watched with amazement as a pickup truck crawled down the bumpy street with a wooden house perched on the bed. Men walked on either side, hands placed against the structure as if they could stop it from falling off. Children darted back and forth, and dogs followed the procession. Goats ripped mouthfuls of grass at the side of the road.

Confusion greeted us as we entered the hospital. It was a single-story, concrete building with wood frame beds on either side of two large rooms. Patients, families and chickens wandered in and out of what should have been isolation areas.

"They are all diar-rating!" a thin woman in a white uniform shouted when she saw our team. The nurse's hands reached out to me. I took a step back. "They're diar-rating everywhere!"

And they were.

Patients were rapidly losing an enormous amount of fluid through yellow, mostly odorless "rice water" diarrhea, the hallmark of Cholera. Too weak to get up, diarrhea poured from beds onto the floor. The ward was a mess.

I couldn't blame the nurse for her frustration. Her small hospital was in chaos. Overwhelmed by one hundred and seventy nine patients in only one week, our Doctors Without Borders/MSF team had been asked to intervene. Our mission was to create a treatment center, institute protocols and train staff to manage the outbreak. If we were successful in stopping the deadly disease our mission would last ten days. If not, hundreds or thousands could potentially die over several months.

"These wooden beds have to be burned," I nodded to the logistician as we did our initial walk through. We had both managed Cholera treatment centers before, and he'd already begun his local purchase list: metal-framed beds, vinyl sheeting with a hole cut in the middle for the patient to lie on, two buckets per bed (one under the hole for diarrhea, one for vomit), powdered chlorine and heavy-duty gloves. Most of the other supplies would be flown in the next day from our Juba stock, but there was no time to waste.

It was all hands on deck. We established "clean" and "dirty" areas, and put handwashing stations wherever a spot could be found. To some family members' dismay, I declared the hospital "animal free." Every time a chicken flapped its wings, I envisioned clumps of microscopic Cholera bacteria flying through the air. The dogs and goats also had to go.

I caught a maintenance man sneaking a wood bed out the back door. I knew it seemed wasteful to destroy such furniture when children slept on straw mats on the floor, but these were impregnated with infectious fluids only killed by burning.

The MSF machine was in full swing. Local staff seemed relieved to have our leadership and worked hard alongside us. Isolating patients, scrubbing floors and walls, digging new latrines, changing buckets: everyone pitched in.

In my hotel room/office, I pulled back the heavy maroon curtains and set to work on reports and paperwork. The hospital was depleted of resources, and I ordered literally tons of supplies. A clanging sound interrupted my focus, and I looked up to see a burlap sack with legs moving across the courtyard. The legs were shackled together and one manacled stick arm dangled links of chain.

Bits of dry grass poked from his filthy dreadlocks, and a wispy beard twitched as he swung his head side to side. He clattered through the empty bar and back out the front gate of the hotel.

On the second day, a nurse told me people were dying in the prison on the other side of town. With our medical and logistic teams fully engaged, I wanted to investigate. The local doctor flared his eyes and vigorously shook his head NO when I asked if he would accompany me.

The door of the prison was imposing. Four times the size of a normal door and made of dark, heavy wood, I could only imagine how many desperate souls had walked across its threshold. My hand looked miniature as I pounded the metal knocker.

A grizzled old man in a stained khaki uniform opened the peephole. From his look and smell, I guessed he was one of the hotel's nightly patrons. Before I could utter a word, he grumbled a rejection.

"May I speak to the medical person in charge of sick prisoners?" I jammed my hand through the opening and offered an MSF card. He snatched it and turned away, leaving the peephole open. I peered in and watched him stagger around a corner, dragging an AK 47 by the barrel.

A uniformed woman wearing flip flops and carrying a chicken under one arm introduced herself as Nurse Esther and showed me to her tiny infirmary. She confirmed they'd had a few cases suspicious of Cholera. "The ones who were throwing and diar-rating went to the hospital for fluids.

"I have so little to offer and no medicines." As she said this, her smile vanished and she grew somber. "A woman was brought for being in a fight and two days later I delivered her baby. There are no gloves, no soap, not even sanitary pads for the women. I used my bandaging supplies to make pads for her."

She told me life in the prison was tough. "If a person steals even ten dollars, they are put in here for six months. Age doesn't matter. Children as young as twelve and thirteen are behind bars. If you murder, you stay for life. Our system is hard."

They received one meal a day - a bowl of beans – and most

prisoners were malnourished. The lucky ones had families who brought in extra food.

"Everything is very hard here."

I gave her all the south Sudanese pounds I had in my pocket (about ten US dollars) and promised to send over gloves, bathing soap, basins and jerry cans for clean water. I would pass her full list of needs to the UN coordinator.

She tied one leg of the chicken to her lopsided wooden desk and escorted me to the gate. The watchman snored from a patch of shade.

Before leaving I thought to ask her about The Clanking Man. "He is in prison so often for his violent behavior, it's easier to subdue him if the shackles stay on."

If you ask me to, I just might change my mind and keep you in my heart forever …

Later in the week over dinner of rice, beans and a nearly meatless chicken leg, our team debriefed the day. Progress had been made. The local ER staff had been trained to screen all people entering the front gates for symptoms and send them to special rehydration stations. The scent of Cholera-killing chlorine infused the facility. More latrines had been dug and pipe had been laid for a new water tank and system. Local staff had recovered from their frazzled state.

Best of all, there were no deaths. We toasted with cold beers.

A very drunken man staggered to my table and fell into a plastic chair. I asked his name and he responded with an incomprehensible grunt. He gestured to the barman and swallowed two beers like a man dying of thirst, then stood and walked out. I was left with the bill. We decided he had wanted to toast our accomplishments too.

As electric light bulbs took over from the sun, I distractedly watched the staff play checkers with red Coke bottle caps vs white water bottle caps. My mind ran in circles of "What if? What next?" when it struck me that Celine had gone silent. I looked around, but no one else seemed to notice. Hard to believe, I missed her.

It's all coming back to me now…

Before the World Tipped

Mariam came to us because she had no lips. She was accompanied by her father, who was anxious to "make her whole" so he could find her a husband. At age nineteen, such a prospect was looking bleak, and she was becoming a burden. Her father spoke for her; since childhood she already had many surgeries to repair a disfiguring congenital cleft lip, but all I could see were her big brown eyes. She was covered in the local tradition, and her father told her to drop her veil.

She held her head high as the fabric was pulled away, revealing a straight line that was her mouth. Her father spoke of her harshly, as if she weren't standing next to him. "No one will consider her this way." She looked down, ashamed.

Ignoring his criticism, I directed my questions to her. "Do you want the Plastic Surgeon to help you? He is very skilled. I've seen him sew together cleft lips and palates, barely leaving a scar. He has changed lives forever." She looked directly at me and tipped her head slightly to the side, a regional gesture indicating an ecstatic nod. I marked her down for a Plastic Surgery consult and asked them to wait in the waiting room.

Here in Lahore, Punjab Province, Pakistan, women and girls cover themselves, and their faces become the sole focus. Shadiha, a bright, chatty seventeen year old, was next for evaluation. Her defect: a corner of her nose missing.

"My father knows best. Without marriage, what value does a woman have? A girl is the property of her father. Then her husband. Once I am whole, my father will find me a suitable husband."

Such is the plight for females in this part of the world. A woman's value is measured by beauty, and utility is reflected in a dowry, or bride price. Any imperfections mar a woman's chance of marriage. To be single means to be shackled to your family forever.

"A girl is not allowed to go outside the house alone or even with girlfriends to have a coffee or to shop for groceries," Shadiha said matter-of-factly. "A brother or male relative must always be at my side, or I will bring dishonor to my family."

I wondered if beneath her confidence was a vulnerable young girl who'd experienced rejection because of a little divot missing from her nose. On most medical missions, "esthetic" plastic surgeries are not performed, but in Pakistan, esthetics are a matter of life and death.

Our surgical mission took place in January 2001, before the world tipped and the towers came down. To be American was to be invincible, but even so, the world was a nebulous place to be on the road less traveled. The Pakistani hospital staff greeted us with open arms but in private said, "We don't like your government, but we love you Americans who come help our children."

Shalamar Hospital was named after the Shalama Gardens. It was a charitable hospital, serving the needs of the poor. With a nursing college and medical school it was the pride of the city, but by American standards it was ramshackle and inefficient. As in most parts of the world, Shalamar Hospital was built over time in fits and spurts as money allowed. The Women's Ward was at one end of a vast hallway; the Men's was down a sloping corridor and past the prayer room with its arrow pointing to Mecca. I often thought I should be like Hansel and Gretel, dropping bread crumbs to find my way back to the Operating Theater. Instead, I relied on friendly staff that went out of their way to help a lost American.

We worked in the hospital for two weeks, bringing the resources and skills needed to perform reconstructive surgeries. Two cases were performed on side by side tables in one OR suite. That way, the team could involve Pakistani surgeons and anesthesiologists, eager to learn new techniques. Surgical masks were placed only over their mouths, and I imagined bacteria blowing out of their noses onto sterile fields. Operating Room shoes were communal: before entering the OR, you left your street shoes on a rack and selected one of the open-toed sandals, well worn by unfamiliar feet. Despite the heat I made sure my mask covered both my mouth and nose, and fresh socks protected my feet in the "slippers."

Nurses wore bubble gum colored salwar kameez: baggy cotton pants tied around the waist with a drawstring and long loose tops draping past the knees. The outfit flattered the tiny frames of the locals, but when I put it on my 5'8" body I felt like an oversized lollipop. The fabric was as soft and comfortable as scrubs at home.

Introductions were made. A Pakistani surgeon offered his labcoat-covered elbow when I held out my hand to shake. I wasn't offended; as a Muslim male he couldn't touch me.

I was assigned as pre-op plus recovery room nurse. Kat, our pediatrician, worked alongside me and floated as the generator monitor. Blackouts were common, sometimes occurring several times in an hour. While we thought it was due to something ominous, the Pakistani surgeon laughingly reassured us it was a result of kite fighting, a popular pastime in the community. Kites would hit an electrical wire and cause a short. When the lights flickered, Kat unwound the stethoscope from her neck and climbed among the octopus of cords and wires to keep the lights on and the essential machinery working.

Many of our patients were children with cleft lips, cleft palates and burn scars needing to be released. Clothing made from polyester, rayon and nylon would easily catch fire from kerosene stoves and heaters, melting onto necks and faces and sticking to tender skin. Many girls and women experienced violence from their domineering husbands, disgruntled suitors or controlling mothers-in-law. Acid or a pan of bubbling oil to the face could change their lives forever. As least we could minimize the disfigurement.

In pre-op, children received grape-flavored Tylenol mixed with the sedative Versed. As they nodded off I started the IV and tucked a beanie baby onto their pillow, whispering a promise to be there when they woke up.

The first two surgeries of any given day were the most complicated and time consuming. After the surgeons started, our

Pediatrician and I went into the wards to check on our post-surgical patients. The female ward was one large open room with six beds facing six more beds. Less-than-comfortable chairs allowed female relatives to guard the patients and tend to their needs. Curtains protected the girls from the casual view of people passing by. The male ward was set up in a similar way without curtains or chairs.

We examined wounds and cleaned suture lines, removed tongue stitches and checked fluid status on cleft palate repairs. I made a habit of hugging everyone, from mothers and grandmothers to nurses and housekeepers. With my statuesque build and long blonde ponytail, they sopped up my attention as if I was a movie star. No hugs were permitted on the male ward.

One girl's grandmother gave me a little mini KitKat candy bar as a thank you. Later, another brought me a carnation. I noticed it had become a competition so graciously refused all gifts. The families had little money, and I didn't want them spending it on unnecessary trinkets.

On the third morning, I was excited to see Mariam's name on the schedule. She was subdued and quiet as I started her IV. I wondered if the three-stage procedure had been explained to her or only to her father. First her tongue would be cut and sewed to the bottom lip. A week later, the piece of tongue would be sliced and lips sewn together. Finally it would be sliced apart and curled to make new lips.

She sailed through the surgeries, but developed complications post-operatively when her tongue was temporarily sewn to both upper and lower lips. A straw slipped through a small slit in the corner of her mouth allowed her to drink, but breathing was possible only through her nose. She would frequently panic and fight to get air. We helped her by cutting a thick plastic endotracheal tube and easing it into the tiny opening between her lips, creating a bigger hole to take deeper breaths.

Mariam was thankful for our help and was generous with hugs. When I asked to have a snap (local slang for "photo") with her, she dropped her gaze and said, "I will tell you tomorrow. First I must ask my father."

She had tried to mehndi henna my palms but the result was rudimentary. One evening she surprised me with her sister, an artist. I lay on the hospital bed in my bubble gum pink scrubs, and allowed her sister to take my hands in hers. She snipped off the top of a henna-filled cone and meticulously squeezed the contents, making intricate designs from fingertips to wrists.

As she worked on my hands, another patient wove a black paranda with tiny mirrors into my hair. The wool braid served to make a woman's hair longer and thicker, a sign of beauty in this culture. But in my blonde locks, it looked like a black animal had nested on my head.

With hands occupied, I asked the pediatrician to pull a little mirrored lipstick case out of my pocket and laughed at the image she showed me. She then moved from bed to bed with the mirror. Post-op lips tilted their heads with satisfaction when they, in turn, looked at their new faces for the first time. My lipstick also passed from hand to hand. Soon everyone from patient to grandma to housekeeper sported bright red mouths, giggling, hugging and laughing. It felt more like a spa than a women's hospital ward.

My hair was a bridge. Women caressed the gold color, and babies reached for it. A young surgical patient was inconsolable until she noticed my blonde ponytail. Her small fingers traveled down the length, twirling it in her fingers. Soon she settled and went to sleep.

On our one day off we were taken for a city tour. The only traffic that didn't stop to stare at us was a sad grey donkey pulling a wooden cart piled high with metal rebar. I wasn't certain if it was because of our white skin or the four armed bodyguards assigned to keep us safe, but wherever we went, crowds gathered. Cameras with telephoto lenses poked out around corners of buildings. Perhaps they thought we were Hollywood stars or royalty because of the big burly men dressed in black who encircled us. The tall blonde with red lipstick was obviously a celebrity. Two men pushed a six year old boy in front of me, snapped a picture, then grabbed the kid and ran off before one of our protectors could get to them.

In one of the city's parks we were treated to an "American picnic" to keep from getting homesick. Even in Pakistan, golden arches on a tan bag were recognizable. While we chewed hamburgers and fries, a group of dirty ragamuffin kids began to gather. They stared intently as we ate, and I felt guilty. Instead of taking the food I offered, they grabbed the large bags and put them on their heads, dancing and singing. I was sad I had no real toys to offer, but the children seemed happy with their new "hats."

The bodyguards grew nervous when we scattered into the market. Unbeknownst to us, there had been a recent increase in violence. Beneath the vibrant city lurked people who set off bombs in marketplaces and kidnapped important people for ransom.

The market was crowded, and the narrow lanes were lined with venders anxious to sell their goods. Every available space was stuffed with merchandise: brightly colored clothes, amazing gold jewelry, incense, children's bicycles, spices and knock-off handbags. Venders called out as we walked by. The women on our team were measured for traditional outfits in black and pearly muted shades with sequins and intricate embroidery. I bought some colorful hand-crafted glass bangles. They came in two sizes – normal and large (for American sized hands). Individually, they were fragile but together they were strong. They tinkled delightfully as I moved.

Our end-of-mission team photo shows us tired but smiling on the hospital front steps. The women all wear long dresses with sleeves covering our arms as we squint into the sun. The hospital administrator smiles radiantly. The eyes of the men in dark suits scan the perimeter. A sign in the background declares, "Bodyguards may not accompany past entrance."

Packing up at the end of a mission always brings mixed emotions. We rarely see the final result of our surgical procedures. Will the teasing end when our children return home? Will the young women find men to embrace and call "husband"? We can only hope our efforts will bring positive change. A blip on the sea of suffering.

A father cornered me as I left the hospital on the final day. I couldn't even remember his child; we'd operated on so many. "Every day for the rest of my life I will pray for the American angels who helped my son."

Nine months later planes took down the World Trade Center and in an instant our world changed forever. America was no long impenetrable. We now knew what others felt for a long, long time. It was a sad day, and the world grieved with us.

In the days after the attack, I mused as to how my life, how anyone's life, can be destroyed by events or circumstances completely out of our control. Every day we have the privilege to reach out to others and heal; to help restore a person facing devastation. All we have to do is look for chances to be of service. To focus on others and not exclusively on ourselves.

That is a choice I learned to make that year.

In the summer of 2006 I received an unexpected phone call from a woman who said she found my name and number online. Apparently, Mariam had asked every American she met to help her, and finally this woman found me. She gave me Mariam's email address, and we began to correspond.

As it turned out, Mariam's recreated lips were a success. She had not only completed her Master's degree in Education but had also married a man who was kind and gentle and loved her.

Miriam emailed me photos of her wedding day. She was beautiful.

Up a River

"Well that was nasty," I laughed as I struggled to climb out of the mud hole I'd just attempted to hop across. "Guess I'm not as young as I thought I was."

A sense of humor goes a long way in the field. I was part of a typical Doctors Without Borders mission: investigate a reported Cholera outbreak in an isolated town surrounded by land mines. Our Spanish logistician Eduardo drove our Land Cruiser and I manned the radio check-in and GPS from the passenger seat. A local translator named Leo squeezed next to Wilbur, our boat driver, among boxes of medical supplies in the back of our vehicle. Five-liter grey metal cans of gasoline and yellow jerry cans of water rode on top, nylon rope threaded through their handles. We pulled a boat behind us that swayed side to side over the hard-packed dirt roads and dry swamp beds. More than once I thought we'd tip, but fortunately Eduardo was skilled at navigating the ruts and furrows.

I thought about asking him to speed up, but didn't. I felt pressured. Time was of the essence. The highest death rate from Cholera occurs in the first days. Even healthy young people can die within hours from dehydration caused by massive diarrhea and vomiting. The sooner we could arrive, the sooner we could begin to implement life-saving actions like oral and IV fluids, boiling and chlorinating water, distributing soap and identifying sick community members. With prevention and rapid, aggressive treatment, survival is possible.

We had to get there fast but it was a tedious eight-hour drive to reach the boat launch site. When we arrived the sun was already low in the sky.

Our first goal was to offload the boat from its trailer into the water, but we'd leave the unloading of the contents of the locked vehicle until morning. Leo searched for twenty able-bodied men among the collection of ramshackle huts and eroded buildings. Unfortunately, happy hour comes early in this isolated village, and there were no sober men to be found. There was nothing to do but wait. We pitched our tents against the vehicle and trailer and retired for the night. I put lotion on my earplugs to drown out tinny transistor radios competing in the cold night air.

A reggae beat from the church woke us at six the next morning. Wishing to avoid the pastor's lecture about demon liquor, men lined up to help load the boat.

"You can do this sister," encouraged one of the men. I leapt forward, missed his outstretched hand and landed in the mud. My white MSF t-shirt was now soaked brown. My blonde hair and jeans were coated with muck. All I could do to preserve my dignity was to laugh.

Wilber started the motor, and we chugged forward.

At last we were on our way up the river

If you look at a map of Ethiopia, the Gambella Region pokes west into South Sudan like a nipple. This remote region is, for the most part, neglected by the dominant Highlanders who maintain political and economic control from the capital city, Addis Ababa. Lowlander tribes are viewed as primitive, uneducated and warlike. The Lowlanders feel marginalized and suppressed by government forces. Conditions have been fertile for conflict since before British colonial rule.

The western Nuer and Anuak tribes coexist, but cows are prioritized over peace. Cattle, the measure of wealth, are exchanged as the bride price, assuring continuation of lineage and culture. With little agriculture, jobs or other means of income, cattle reign supreme. Cattle-raiding between tribes is commonplace, but since success brings instant wealth, these raids become an exercise in tit for tat.

Temporary cattle camps follow the grass. When it is dry, animals graze near a stream or river. When the rains come, the animals get stuck in the mud or sick from biting flies so they must be moved to higher ground or die. At night, cows are tethered to wooden pegs pounded into the ground in the center of the compound. Herders erect straw huts on the periphery "circle the wagons" style. During the night, marauders sneak in, cut the ropes and steal the cows. Huts are set ablaze, possessions charred, and many who attempt to flee are killed.

The miserable rainy season brings peace from lack of mobility. Enormous herds of the beasts need extensive grazing land that is only accessible during the October-April dry season. When the rains begin, the black cotton soil becomes a thick, sticky muck with a foot of water atop, impassible for cattle and man.

Thus, he who stole last wins.

The Akobo River divides this area of Ethiopia from eastern South Sudan where the Murle tribesmen forage with their herds in much the same manner. Cross-river cattle raids between tribes are ignored by the central governments, despite catastrophic loss of life and decimation of villages. Perception of "good guy" and "bad guy" varies, depending on which side of the river you stand. One side's dominant group is viewed as murdering thieves by the other side and vice versa.

Against this backdrop, Doctors Without Borders provides essential medical services to both sides of the river in its typical neutral fashion. When Cholera was reported in Akobo on the South Sudan side of the river, it fell to me, as Project Coordinator in Ethiopia, to investigate the outbreak.

Our boat was not built for comfort. A flat fifteen-foot rig, it had a small canopy to protect from the blaring heat of the sun, depending on its position in the sky. Jerry cans crammed the bottom, some filled with drinking water and others with fuel for the journey. We jockeyed for space around boxes of medical supplies, tents and our personal carryall packs. Wilbur navigated from the outboard motor in the back. According to the men at the boat launch, we should reach Akobo in eight hours. When I asked about food, Eduardo assured me we'd find women willing to cook for us en route.

The river teemed with wildlife. Dozens of varieties of birds inspected our craft as we puttered along. Pelicans hopped across the water surface before launching into flight. A tall stork-like bird with an eight-foot wingspan stomped the river's edge. Huge snoutless lizards swam alongside, then vanished into the water with a splash of their tails. Fish jumped into the boat. The air was filled with biting flies and mosquitos, leaving inflamed welts on our skin. The sun was sweltering.

"You can endure anything for eight hours," I thought as I rubbed a new bruise on my leg from the corner of a box. I busied myself by thinking of my strategy for implementing care when we arrived.

Human life also abounded along the riverbanks. Bands of naked children waved and shouted from the waterline while their partially clothed parents stood back and stared. Although our vantage point was ten feet below ground level, we could still see the edge of massive cattle camps on the high banks. Herds were tended by boys armed with sticks, playing at being men with spears. Wisps of smoke rose from distant cooking fires under straw lean-tos.

A few hours along our journey, the cattle camps gave way to a spotty collection of typical African dried-mud tukuls. Fishermen strung nets from one side of the river to the other. While it was an effective technique to catch fish, the nets inhibited our passage. Every ten to twenty yards, Wilbur had to throw the outboard engine into neutral, raise it out of the water and glide over the tops of the nets. Unfortunately, the nets would occasionally get entangled in the propeller and halt our progress. Leo called out in local dialects to the wary villagers, telling them we would not do any damage. One old man, naked except for a loincloth, charged our boat shouting and threatening us with a spear. Wilber hastily cut the net and powered upriver, until we were forced to stop for another net.

The fishermen's nets had slowed our progress. I urged Wilbur to speed up, but he continued at a snail's pace. The longer we were delayed, the more people would die. I was growing irritated by the bug bites, the sweltering heat and crowded conditions. I picked mud flakes off my jeans and ignored the need to pee.

Another obstacle lay ahead. The river's surface was covered in water hyacinths – masses of tightly packed floating plants that extended miles. We were able to push through some of the smaller clumps using only the motor, but the wind and current had packed some areas so tightly, we had to use a pole and oars to push our way through. Progress was painfully slow. In one area, the vegetation was so thick, the three men stripped to their underwear, jumped into the water and pulled the boat along. I briefly considered plunging into the cool water but given my recent mud puddle jumping adventure, I figured I'd probably drown. The men were fortunate: they were able to relieve their bladders while in the water. I wondered how much longer I could wait.

Ten hours had passed, and our destination was nowhere in sight. Huge black clouds billowed in the sky and the wind picked up. I wanted to continue, but Wilbur convinced me we would be in jeopardy if the boat was out in the river when the storm arrived. He steered to the bank and climbed out, pounded pegs into the soft earth and tied ropes front and back. We scrambled to unload our tents and backpacks as the clouds rushed us. It smelled like rain. The wind tugged as I secured the frames of the tents around the only sturdy tree we could find. I watched my nylon tent puff up like a pillow then deflate as if it was going to fly away.

Eduardo was wrong. Rather than offering food, women along the way hid when they saw us. We pulled a few BP5 biscuits from the medical kits for malnourished patients. Fortunately, I'd thought to stash a few tiny tins of tuna, part of a care package I'd received from Canadian friends a week earlier. Inside my tent, I flicked on my headlamp, struggled out of my crusty clothes and crawled into my sleeping bag. I fell asleep reading a book about Shackleton and his trip to Antarctica, where he explored ice and snow instead of bug-infected rivers.

River day two was painfully slow. The water plants, even more densely packed by the storm, choked our passage. Our stomachs growled, and tempers were short. My skin crawled with bug bites, and my clothes crunched with dried mud. While the men could turn their backs to relieve themselves, the boat had to be beached for my bathroom needs. I had to climb the bank and search for a shrub or tree wide enough to hide my bare white bottom. Tugging sweat-soaked jeans down and up required a fair amount of wiggling and hopping. I balanced my water intake against dehydration.

Bathing was also easier for the men. They jumped into the river with a bar of soap. I, on the other hand, had to haul a bucket of the brownish water up the bank, find another tree, strip naked behind its precarious shelter, then pour plastic cupfuls over my head and body. I refused to entertain the notion that the water cascading over me was the same as the Cholera-carrying water further upriver. I vowed to cut my long hair as soon as we returned "home" to Gambella.

For one such bathroom break, Wilbur pulled into a clump of weeds and was attacked by a frenzy of bees, buzzing and stinging until his face was lumpy and eyes swollen nearly shut. I gave him Benadryl, which reduced the swelling but made him so drowsy, we had to stop for a second night.

Leo cooked a fish he bought from a woman along the river. He made a lavish display of building a fire and cooking the fish in the coals. It smelled burnt and looked awful, so I stayed in my tent, feasting on tinned tuna and a few stale almonds from a pocket of my pack.

By the third day on the river, we travelled in silence. Wilber's face was still red and puffy. All he needed was a corncob pipe and can of spinach and he'd be the spitting image of an African Popeye. He said he was ready to drive, and I thought to myself, "He wants to get there as badly as the rest of us."

No one had a story to tell or a joke to share. All eyes focused ahead, as if our wills would help propel the boat. Earlier in the morning we spoke to a group of Ethiopian troops patrolling the eastern bank. Leo told them of our mission and asked if they'd experienced any vomiting or diarrhea. With serious faces, they waved us on our way. An hour later, we saw Sudanese soldiers walking the west side.

Under the sweltering sun, I mused about life on the river. Cows looked the same on both sides – gray and brown and thin. People looked the same. Similar languages, similar features except for face tattooing on one side and scarification on the other. But people view "others" as different, as murderers, cattle thieves to be afraid of and protected against. From a distance everything looks the same.

People who travel for pleasure often say, "It's not about the destination, it's about the journey." This trip was far from pleasure. It was about the destination.

Near dusk, our backs straightened and eyes grew sharp. If we'd had antennae, they would have pricked forward. Concrete-block buildings sprang from the ground where before we'd only seen clusters of tukuls. School uniforms adorned staring children. Adults waved without spears in hand. A painted sign read: Akobo General Store. We'd arrived.

We asked directions to the health center and were waved generally "there." Hauling our cramped legs from the boat, we made our way to what appeared to be a bombed out concrete structure, now covered in moss and the black stains of abandonment. Eduardo and I looked at each other – would this intervention require rebuilding of a health structure in addition to hands on medical care? We immediately began to scan dimensions and formulate tentative plans of action.

On the far side of the buildings, we stopped dead in our tracks. We were too late. Another organization arrived before us and set up a treatment unit. They greeted us with the familiar elbow tap "handshake" of Cholera outbreaks. With a quick glance at our grubby attire, they assured us mitigation steps were already underway.

Relieved but unneeded, we turned and started the long trip back down the river.

Of Mugs and Men

Sue was in the middle of her four month Philippines mission when things went from bad to worse back home. I hesitated to tell her that our pleasant little ER had crumbled. Dana, recently promoted to ER manager, insisted on high scores on patient satisfaction surveys. She only agreed with the first half of our "Work hard, play harder" philosophy.

We nurses have always believed that supporting, encouraging and mentoring the ER staff results in higher quality patient care. Happy nurse = Happy patient. The hallmark of an Emergency Room nurse is to try to find the humor in any situation. Playing doesn't negate our skills - it's how we cope. To the unobservant eye, our humor may be dark or biting, but our laughter prevents us from drowning in a sea of tragedy.

ER culture was changing across the country. Skills mattered less than patients being happy with their care, and financial reimbursement was tied to Press Ganey survey satisfaction scores. One patient complained her pain had not been controlled with high doses of narcotics, despite being so sedated, she had to be placed on oxygen and physically roused to breathe. Another patient complained the turkey sandwich the nurse gave him was cold. Dana counseled the nurses when these patients left unhappy.

If I told Sue about the erosion of the ER, she would be frustrated at not being able to help from so far away. Besides, so many great things had happened for her: a new hip (thanks to a fabulous orthopedic surgeon) and a new man (thanks to Craigslist).

An upcoming article in the hospital newsletter was also in the works, showcasing her as "Staff Star" for her work on humanitarian missions. For over a decade, Sue had worked a concentrated schedule which freed her to volunteer in dozens of countries across Africa, Asia and Latin America.

"You lead an exciting life," the hospital newsletter reporter said during her interview, shaking her head over photographs from one of the trips.

"'Exciting' in the context where I volunteer usually means 'danger,'" Sue said with a shrug. "I prefer to say I lead a 'valuable' life. Or a 'life of service.'

Soon she would be in the midst of a religious war in the Philippines, but first came The Great Mugnapping.

I had given our unit clerk a gift to celebrate his twenty-fifth birthday: a dainty pink coffee mug with the silhouette of a black cat sitting on a fence, long swooping tail trailing down the handle. Al, a tattooed young man with spiked hair and muscular build, said it was the best gift he'd ever received.

"It's a panther," he countered whenever anyone commented on the feminine mug. "It's stealthy and powerful, like me."

"No, it's a kitty sitting on a fence," we'd laugh.

"It's ready to pounce at any given moment. These marks?" He pointed to the paw prints that climbed around the inside. "They're made by sharp claws that could rip out your jugular. "

Then he'd take a delicate sip holding up his pinky.

He loved that mug, but one day I noticed him drawing a stick-figure cat on the side of a Styrofoam cup.

"Where is your kitty mug?" I asked.

"You mean my *panther* mug." he replied. With a quick glance at Dana's closed door, he whispered, "She took it."

"You distract Dana," Sue said after I told her about Al's missing mug. "Get her out of her office. Tell her someone didn't label the multi-dose vials of medication. I'll do the rest."

Sue had been the instigator of multitudes of gags over the years, keeping department morale high. Each May, National Nurses Day is celebrated with luncheons, grateful speeches for the often tireless work of nurses, and touching gifts given by thankful management staff. That year, the hospital delivered each nurse a box of animal crackers and a juice cup. No luncheon. No speeches. In response, we filmed a video montage of staff interviews, expressing why they loved working in our Emergency Room. Every nurse got a copy.

The film's ending showed our heart: Trauma One in post-resuscitation chaos, equipment alarming, cardiac monitor leads on the floor, hissing oxygen tubes, counter littered with used trays, floor covered with equipment wrappers and blood. The patient had been a young woman on birth control pills who had just flown in from New York City. The pain in her leg was so intense, her husband had called 911. By the time the paramedics arrived, the blood clot had travelled to her lungs. Our resuscitation failed.

No one laughed that day.

Sue decided we'd gone long enough without playing. Snatching the mug from Dana's office was the easy part, but listening to her lecture on the importance to adhering to policy was painful. She'd also tossed an open bottle of Maalox into the trash when she found the lid off in the medication room. "Someone probably drank right from the bottle!"

Two minutes after returning to her office, her door opened again. She scanned the nurse's station and found only angelic faces hard at work. Al focused on his computer screen.

"Can't believe you guys did that," he whispered under his breath. "This isn't going to end well."

The pink kitty mug was nowhere to be found. Sue and I played innocent when Dana asked about it during a team huddle. She scoured the break room, looking through seldom used cupboards. Nor was it among the discarded mugs, chipped or deemed inappropriate for displaying slogans such as "You May Not Like Me, But I'll Save Your Life" or "I'm Here To Save Your Ass, Not Kiss It." She asked some of the more compliant nurses and techs, but no one would confess.

In a private conversation with Dana, Sue suggested that staff was playing with her and joining in the game might help build a stronger team. Dana's smile was not encouraging.

After that, the Great Mugnapping went full throttle. Other staff were kept apprised of our antics. The next morning, Dana listened to a message on her voicemail. The voice was male, deep and threatening.

"I've got the mug. It is safe ... *for now.* Bring chocolate for the staff or you'll never see the pink kitty again."

Dana walked the unit with a scowl on her face. She chastised Al for not using her approved scripted responses when answering the telephone. She snapped at nurses for minor infractions. Her attention turned to me; I was no longer allowed to label my water bottle "VODKA."

When Dana arrived the following day, a photo was taped to her office door: the pink kitty mug, silhouetted against a white screen, orange scarf blindfolding its eyes, and a "proof of life" newspaper with the current date alongside.

"Okay, this isn't funny," Dana announced at the nurse's station. There were muffled giggles, and eyes turned downward. "If you guys would spend as half as much energy taking care of patients as you do with these silly games, imagine how good our Press Ganey numbers would be." She retreated to her office, slamming the door behind her.

Our laughter was interrupted by the arrival of Medic One. With military precision, we turned and entered the Trauma room.

At the end of the week, a treasure hunt appeared, leading Dana from the Code Cart to the Medication Room to other potential hiding spots. It ended at the staff lounge freezer, where the Pink Kitty Mug was "on ice" along with a pound of fresh roasted coffee. Dana grabbed them without a word and shut herself into her office.

Life and work went on, and Sue dubbed herself "Quasimodo." During her last mission in Sudan, a grabbing pain in her groin twisted her foot outward causing a lurching, rocking gait. At 53, she needed a hip replacement. She dropped her Leave of Absence paperwork into Dana's mailbox.

To entertain ourselves in the Pre-Op waiting area, I typed as she dictated an online ad for Craigslist's "Women Looking for Men" section. In her hospital room after surgery, as she lay immobilized, we scrutinized the responses. With each "delete" she laughingly pushed her pain mediation button.

Delete. Delete. Delete. Pause. What? Had she found the needle in the haystack of men? She met Pete a week later, and they were inseparable until she left a month later for her new mission. Ten years out of the dating game, Sue packed new emotions along with her bags.

After Sue's departure, I watched as changes were implemented in the hospital. Budget cuts targeted lower paid employees first. Cafeteria, laundry and housekeeping functions were outsourced. We lost our beloved Maria, who had been our ER housekeeper for years.

Older, more expensive, and often more outspoken nurses were next on the chopping block. One nurse was counseled after forgetting to clock out for lunch. Another was taken to Human Resources and told she needed to smile more. Three ICU nurses were terminated for not documenting wasted narcotics "in a timely manner," implying they had diverted the drugs for personal use; a black mark that could end a nurse's career.

"I've seen this before," a nurse, two years from retirement, said."In California. They made nurses take a test where you'd have to manually figure out IV drip rates. Mcg/kg/min. We haven't had to do that since nursing school! I passed, but several other didn't and were fired. It's an easy way to trim the budget."

Dana walked past just as Al massaged a muscle I'd pulled in my shoulder while transferring a large woman from wheelchair to stretcher. "What would you think if you saw the servers massaging each other in a fine dining restaurant?"

After a patient complained about loud voices in the nurse's station, Dana placed a toy traffic light on the counter. Figuring it had been effective in hushing her daughter's first grade class, Dana was confident it would work on us. When the light turned yellow, we were to quiet our voices. Red meant we were out of control. Only a passive green was acceptable.

The light lasted less than twenty four hours. Someone on the evening shift placed it in the ambulance bay. Cheers erupted as it was crushed beneath the wheels of Medic One.

Sue and I were in frequent touch via Skype and email. I told her lighthearted stories and gossip, but didn't tell her morale was at an all-time low over reallocation of nurse's rotations.

The atmosphere in Mindanao, she told me, was tense. Muslim insurgents had been fighting for independence from the strict Catholic government for years. Her Doctors Without Borders team provided daily medical care to hundreds of civilians displaced by the fighting. "These poor people are under constant stress," Sue said. "Shelling and gunfire are every day occurrences."

The heavily religious government had also imposed severe restrictions on reproductive rights, even imprisoning doctors for discussing abortion with women who begged for the procedure. Illegality lead to unclean and unsafe, and it was the women who suffered most. Physical abuse was commonplace as was heavy alcohol consumption. "MUPS", Medically Unexplained Physical Symptoms, was frequency diagnosed and triggered psychologists to be involved in the plan of care. I wondered if this approach would be helpful for some patients in our ER: those with undiagnosed abdominal pain, chronic headaches, back pain or anyone that required high doses of narcotics to ease their symptoms. Sadly, it also occurred to me it might also be useful for some of our stressed out staff members.

Cholera had come with the rainy season in Mindanao, and their team mobilized responses to isolated areas. Sue downplayed the physical threats she and her team were under. I researched online about the area she worked: bombs were detonated in public areas creating widespread panic. In the resulting chaos, people would be snatched unnoticed. Kidnapping for ransom was a common means to finance the resistance.

"Are you safe?" I asked during a Skype conversation. "I heard about the kidnappings of foreign aid workers."

"Of course," she laughed. "It's all about staying alert and not being scared. I got the team focused on a scarf instead of being afraid when they started shelling near us. Remember that bright orange scarf we blindfolded the Pink Kitty with? I have it here."

She'd started a game to find creative uses for the scarf and took photos of staff members using it as an 80's headband, a flag, a bra, a napkin, a blanket and pillow. She emailed me her favorite picture of herself: the scarf covered her head like a nun, her eyes gazed upward to heaven, hands together as in prayer. She'd never looked so saintly. She used their pictures to create a "Kidnapping Survival Strategy" PowerPoint presentation and sent it to Geneva headquarters.

"How are things?" she asked. "Tell me everything."

"You know," I hedged. "Same thing on a different day."

I didn't tell her about the erosion of care that had occurred with management pressure to redirect our focus from patient care to customer service. Nurses were kept busy fetching blankets and fluffing pillows instead of having time to adequately assess higher acuity patients. Necessary care was delayed, and patients backed up in the hallways.

But my heart broke over a sixteen-year old Guatemalan girl who came during the overnight shift with chest pain. It wasn't until a Spanish speaking housekeeper arrived for 7am day shift that her mother could explain that her daughter was breathing funny and was in acute respiratory distress. She died four hours later.

I showed Dana the chart; initial vital signs clearly showed the young girl was in serious trouble. "This is what happens when you stress customer service over critical thinking," I said.

Dana thanked me for bringing the situation to her attention. Two weeks later I was suspended for crinkling papers during a meeting.

I decided I would wait to tell Sue about all of this when she returned. With only three weeks left to her mission she had accomplished her goals for establishing the Mindanao team and had relocated to Manila to construct a permanent coordination team. Their advocacy efforts would be more effective in the capital, with access to various branches of government and other agencies. In preparation for her return, Sue emailed Dana to request shifts on the upcoming schedule.

One Saturday morning I received a text: "*Wrapping up in Manila. Coming home soon. No word from Dana. Raining like crazy! Can't see out the window.*" That was the last I heard from her for days.

Typhoon Ondoy hit the island with record breaking winds and rain. I read in the paper the government was caught off guard. When torrential rains threatened to overwhelm dams on the rivers, they opened the floodgates. Walls of water, twelve to fifteen feet high, swept homes, crops and people into the ocean. The army recovered three hundred and fifty-eight bodies, mostly poor folks who lived in shanties at bends in the rivers where water naturally slowed. Manila's inadequate drainage system collapsed under the flood burden, and the entire capital stood four feet under sewage-tainted water.

Sue led the emergency response team, travelling in makeshift boats to various stranded neighborhoods, delivering medical supplies and treating the ill and injured. Families crowded into second floor school classrooms, upper bleachers at soccer stadiums and even built shelters in trees to escape snakes and other vermin in the floodwaters. The emergency response group from Geneva headquarters arrived within the week with supplies and manpower to relieve exhausted team members.

Spent and experiencing pain in her post-op hip, Sue checked her emails. The one from Dana read: "*Your employment has been terminated as I did not approve your Leave of Absence request.*"

The ER was rocked. It was the horse head beneath the sheets.

Staff protests turned into whispers, which turned into silence. The unspoken message shouted loud and clear: if you don't like it you can leave.

Although I was reinstated, I felt the target on my back.

The nurse's union was unsuccessful in negotiating Sue's rehire, but that disappointment evaporated at the airport. Her new Craigslist guy, Pete, was there to pick her up.

But the story doesn't end there.

One overwhelmingly busy evening shift, a grinning ED tech handed me the newest issue of the hospital newsletter. Under the "STAFF STAR" headline grinned Sue, wearing an orange scarf and holding a baby she'd delivered in Darfur on her first mission. The reporter had been so impressed, she'd given her top billing above the Letter from the CEO. The article was a glowing report about Sue's journeys and her positive influence in the hospital's Emergency Room.

It didn't take long until there was a flurry of activity. Managers were instructed to retrieve all the magazines from the foyers and patient rooms. The tech dashed around ahead of them, grabbing as many as she could, and delivered them into my welcoming arms.

"Typical corporate snafu," Sue said when I told her. "Left hand not knowing what the right hand's doing. Nobody really cares."

But I did.

I picked her up for coffee. She talked about the needless suffering she'd seen. People lived in deplorable conditions.

Kidnapping was real and often ended with death. Her stories were heartbreaking and painfully real. I told her the truth about what had happened to our ER in her absence. Then I glanced at my watch and told her we had an appointment nearby.

In the sound station of the NPR studio, you could hear a pin drop. We were fitted with headphones and microphones. For an hour Sue answered questions about the typhoon response, the tragic deaths and the urgent rescue of stranded families. The reporter asked how it felt to be featured by the hospital that just fired her for doing the work they heralded her for. The irony was obvious.

"I just wanted my job back, but my heart is in humanitarian work," Sue said. "I can find an ER job anywhere. But if I can make a dent in the life of someone who has suffered so much – that's a real victory. Small ripples make the world a better place."

The piece ran several times a day for a week. A local TV station covered the story and quoted the hospital spokesperson, "No comment."

A pink coffee mug with the curling tail of a black cat sits on my kitchen windowsill. As Sue said, sometimes the best you can get is a small victory. And I hope that the battle, which started out as a harmless mugnapping, ended in just that.

Six years later, Sue shocked me with an announcement: Pete had asked her to marry him. Their unwritten pre-nup ensures she can continue to volunteer with Doctors Without Borders and run her nonprofit organization, One Nurse At A Time. It seems she really may have found the needle in the haystack.

Our heartfelt thanks for the keen eyes of Pete Bartnick, Karen Heileson, Erin Neoh, Staci Kelley and Nancy Harless who helped us edit this book.

We also thank nurses everywhere for their selfless and often overlooked contributions to our lives and health, and the lives and health of others across our globe.

Donations to support our work can be made at www.OneNurseAtATime.org

Sue Averill RN

Growing up as an army brat gave me a love for travel and other cultures which was cemented by living in Mexico two years as a young woman. I wanted to be a nurse from age five and started my ER nursing career in 1979. In response to the devastating 1985 earthquake in Mexico City, I organized and lead a 21 person team providing medical care in collaboration with The Salvation Army – my first foray into the humanitarian arena.

After obtaining an MBA and a stint in the business world, I decided to dedicate more of my time to humanitarian medical work: teaching in Cambodia, surgical and medical trips to Asia, Africa and Latin America, and helping to design medical clinics in Honduras and Vietnam. I consider myself a "Humanitarian Snowbird" – escaping Seattle winters by working for Doctors Without Borders and other volunteer organizations in warmer venues around the world.

The key for me came during a surgical trip to Pakistan – by comparison to girls and women there, I have lived a charmed life.

I was born in a time and place that fosters independence, education and freedom for women. I believe it to be my responsibility to give of myself for the many gifts that I have received through no merit of my own.

One Nurse At A Time grew out of frequent inquiries by others "How can I get involved and do what you do?" Our goal is to make it easier for nurses to use their skills to help people around the world, to lower the entry barriers, to increase public awareness of the role and contribution nurses make in the humanitarian world.

I truly believe we CAN change the world.

Elizabeth Coulter RN

Elizabeth Coulter made the life changing decision to become a Registered Nurse at 30 years of age. After graduating from Red Deer College in Alberta, Canada, she worked in England, and continues to alternate between emergency departments in Canada and the United States.

Her first medical mission was as a recovery room nurse for facial reconstructive surgery in an orphanage in China, which is the setting for her first published work "Mai Mai" in Beyond Borders. On a later teaching mission to Vietnam, she appreciated the graciousness of the nurses and their eagerness to learn, despite lacking the tools to implement what they were taught.

Elizabeth studied Created Writing at the University of Washington, and resides in Vancouver, Canada. She is currently working on her first novel.